The Observer Book of SPACE

Editor
Carl Wilkinson

Contributors
Leslie Cantwell; Dr Michael Foale; Professor Ofer Lahav; Robin McKie;
Dr Edgar Mitchell; Sir Patrick Moore; Ian Pearson; George Pendle;
Professor Colin Pillinger; Neil Spencer; Tom Templeton

Observer Books
Lisa Darnell

Sub-editor
Leah Jewett

Researchers
Edward Coles, Jemma Foster, James Fulker, Tessa Harris

First published by Observer Books 2007
Observer Books is an imprint of Guardian News and Media

Printed and bound in the UK by Cox & Wyman Ltd, Reading, Berkshire

Pictures: Esa, Nasa, The Art Archive, Bettmann/Corbis, Kobal, Getty Images, Rex Features, Hulton, PA, AP, Twentieth Century Fox, Reuters

The cover shows a column of cool molecular hydrogen gas and dust that acts as an incubator for new stars in the Eagle Nebula M16, about 7,000 light years from Earth. The photograph was taken on 1 April 1995 by the Hubble Space Telescope

Cover design: Two Associates
Text design: seagulls.net
Graphics: Cath Levett
Picture research: Sarah King

Introduction

The sheer scale of the universe and our place in it has long puzzled philosophers, scientists and amateur stargazers alike. It is hard, when looking skywards on a clear night, not to ponder the large questions Douglas Adams put so memorably in *The Hitchhiker's Guide to the Galaxy* – those of 'life, the universe and everything'.

How can the universe be so vast and human beings so seemingly inconsequential, yet as far as we know alone, on a relatively insignificant planet in a small arm of a minor galaxy? As the early astronomer Galileo put it: 'The Sun, with all the planets revolving around it and depending on it, can still ripen a bunch of grapes as though it had nothing else in the universe to do.'

In this book, we look at the science behind space – black holes, dark matter, supernovae – our ongoing exploration of our solar system, and what the future holds for manned missions to the Moon and beyond. We talk to insiders who have blasted off into orbit, lived onboard the International Space Station, set foot on the Moon or simply toured the heavens with the aid of star charts, telescopes and not a little imagination. We explore the nascent space tourism industry and offer a more esoteric perspective on space: UFO encounters, alien abduction and science fiction.

Welcome to *The Observer Book of Space*.

A–Z of space

A **Astronomical Unit (AU)** A unit based on our distance from the Sun. The Earth is 1AU from the Sun; Neptune is 30.06 AUs away.

B **Big Bang** The theory explaining how an infinitesimally small, infinitely hot and infinitely dense singularity expanded rapidly around 13.7 billion years ago to create the still-expanding universe.

C **Comets** Icy lumps of dust, water and gas, originating in the Oort cloud, a spherical shell surrounding the solar system thought to contain 10 trillion comets. They can be seen from Earth every five to six years as they form a bright tail of gas.

D **Dark matter** A theoretical substance that accounts for 90% of the matter in the universe and is technically invisible.

E **Eclipse** A solar eclipse occurs when the Moon passes in front of the Sun, blocking out light. Total eclipses occur somewhere on Earth every 18 months, but will only recur in the same place every 370 years. The next eclipse will be on 1 August 2008; it will be visible in the UK as a partial eclipse.

F **Falling stars** Meteors made of rock and iron burning up in the Earth's atmosphere. Also known as shooting stars.

G **Galaxy** A collection of billions of stars all gravitationally bound together. Our solar system's home galaxy is the Milky Way.

H **Hubble constant (H_0)** The rate at which the universe is expanding, as discovered by Edwin Hubble and Milton Humason in 1929. The most recent (accurate) observation was that it is expanding at a rate of 71km/second/Mpc (see Parsec).

I **Ion engine** Electrically charged engines which propel spacecraft by firing positive ions. Although their power is minute – the thrust is comparable to the pressure of a piece of paper on your hand – ion engines are incredibly efficient, and can travel faster and further than other forms of rocket.

J **Jovian planet** Any of the four outer 'gas giants' – Jupiter, Saturn, Uranus and Neptune.

K **Kuiper belt** A large ring of icy objects surrounding our solar system and thought to be debris from its creation.

L **Light year** The distance that light travels in one year, or 5,878,625,373,183.61 (5.8 trillion) miles.

M **Messier number** Eighteenth-century astronomer Charles Messier listed the positions of about 100 mysterious objects he discovered while hunting for comets. Now known to be among the brightest star clusters, galaxies and nebulae, they are still known by the number Messier gave them (eg the Andromeda galaxy is M31).

N **Neutron star** After a massive star has exploded as a supernova, the collapsed core is so compressed that atoms are crushed, fusing the protons and electrons to leave only neutrons.

O **Orbit** The path of a planet or satellite around another object such as the Sun. The orbits of the planets are elliptical, not circular.

P **Parsec (pc)** A large-distance unit equal to 3.26 light years. Also kpc (3,260 light years) and Mpc (3,260,000 light years).

Q **Quasar (quasi-stellar radio object)** An incredibly bright object lying at the furthest reaches of the universe, it is not powered by a star but by the black hole which lies at its centre. The friction from matter sucked into black holes produces a brilliant glow.

R **Radio bubble** A sphere of radio waves centred on Earth. Its outer edges correspond with the first man-made signals that escaped the Earth's atmosphere. Travelling at the speed of light, the bubble has reached beyond Alpha Centauri (our nearest star system).

S **Scintillation** Known commonly as the twinkling of stars, this is caused by a star's light being distorted by the Earth's atmosphere.

T **Transit** The passage of one heavenly body in front of another. Mercury can be seen passing across the Sun approximately 13 times every century.

U **Universal Time (UT)** The standard time zone used by all astronomers. It is the same as Greenwich Mean Time (GMT).

V **Virgo cluster** A gigantic cluster of more than 2,000 galaxies, found within the constellation of Virgo.

W **Wormholes** Huge amounts of mass can warp the fabric of space, essentially allowing matter to jump from one region of space to another millions of light years away through wormholes.

X **X-ray star** A bright star that gives off X-rays as the largest proportion of its radiation.

Y **Ylem (or yelm)** The name given to the hypothetical original matter from which all elements were formed.

Z **Zenith** The point directly above your head in the night sky.

Space timeline

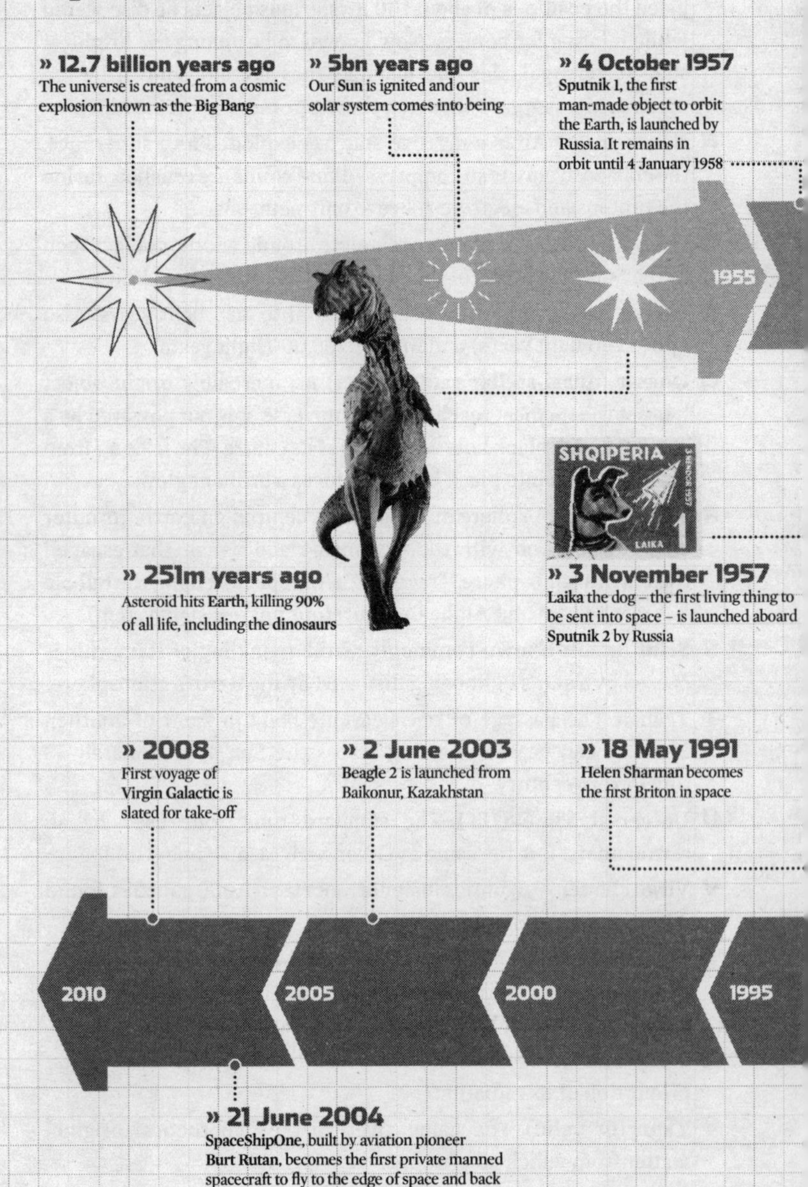

» 12.7 billion years ago
The universe is created from a cosmic explosion known as the Big Bang

» 5bn years ago
Our Sun is ignited and our solar system comes into being

» 4 October 1957
Sputnik 1, the first man-made object to orbit the Earth, is launched by Russia. It remains in orbit until 4 January 1958

» 251m years ago
Asteroid hits Earth, killing 90% of all life, including the dinosaurs

» 3 November 1957
Laika the dog – the first living thing to be sent into space – is launched aboard Sputnik 2 by Russia

» 2008
First voyage of Virgin Galactic is slated for take-off

» 2 June 2003
Beagle 2 is launched from Baikonur, Kazakhstan

» 18 May 1991
Helen Sharman becomes the first Briton in space

» 21 June 2004
SpaceShipOne, built by aviation pioneer Burt Rutan, becomes the first private manned spacecraft to fly to the edge of space and back

31 January 1958
plorer 1, the first US satellite in
it, lifts off from Cape Canaveral
ng a modified ABMA-JPL
iter-C rocket. It carries a scientific
eriment designed by James A Van
n, which discovers the Earth's
iation belt

» 5 June 1961
Britain successfully launches an unmanned rocket, Blue Streak, from Australia

» 23 November 1963
First episode of the *Doctor Who* series airs in the UK

» 6 April 1968
Stanley Kubrick's *2001: A Space Odyssey* premieres

1960

1965

1970

1975

1980

1985

1990

» 20 July 1969
Neil Armstrong and Edwin 'Buzz' Aldrin become the first humans to land on the Moon. They make the first moonwalk on the following day

» 12 April 1961
The Soviets win the race to put first man in space. Cosmonaut Yuri Gargarin orbits Earth once before returning safely

» 18 March 1965
The first spacewalk is made from Soviet Voskhod 2 by Cosmonaut Alexei Leonov. It lasts just 12 minutes

October 1958
National Aeronautics and
ce Administration (Nasa) is
nded, taking over from the
ional Advisory Committee
Aeronautics

» 16 June 1963
Soviet cosmonaut Valentia Tereshkova becomes the first woman in space. She orbits the Earth 48 times onboard Vostok 6

» 24 April 1990
Hubble Space Telescope is launched

» 25 January 1986
The US space shuttle Challenger explodes minutes after take-off, killing all seven astronauts on board

» 25 May 1977
George Lucas' *Star Wars* film premieres

The insider: astronaut

Mike Foale

I always wanted to be an astronaut. My mum's American, and I picked up the idea in the States – that desire was fostered by my parents and my American grandma, who gave me books on astronomy. The other career concept I had was to try to cure cancer. It was that or space, whichever was going to be easier.

Astronauts need to be renaissance people. I studied physics at the Cavendish labs in Cambridge, learned to fly, scuba dive, explore. But on a motivational level it was science fiction that really fired me up: I read *Starman Jones* (Robert A Heinlein's book for children) when I was 11, *Biggles* and all the good English adventure stuff. I'm a great romantic and love adventure stories, but I'm sad to say the whole point of all the training we do is to not become terrified. As an astronaut you are predictable: you do exactly what you've been asked to do.

> *"It's human nature to stretch, to go, to see, to understand. Exploration is not a choice, really; it's an imperative.*
> Apollo 11 astronaut Michael Collins

My first launch was in Atlantis in 1992, on a mission called Atlas 1. You're on your back and pointing straight up – all you can see is blue sky. Once the solid rocket booster is lit, it's a huge kick in the back. The first surprise was that I couldn't read the instruments because they were shaking so much. Then you feel your head spinning as you go through a half roll and pull over the Atlantic, increasing speed so that by the time the solid rocket boosters are tailing off you've hit 3gs, which feels like having three people sitting on your chest – there's a big poof of flame outside, and then it goes all quiet.

At that point we open up our visors and can talk across the air path to each other not using microphones. As the fuel is used up, the whole vehicle becomes lighter and then the engines at the back of the shuttle start to accelerate you, and by the time it's over – 6.5 minutes after the separation of the boosters (a total of 8.5 minutes) – you feel 3gs on your chest again. Then all of a sudden the engine cuts off and your hands fly up in front of your face as you become weightless and you're fumbling around like a klutz trying to take your helmet off, put it in a bag and get on with your job.

It's not claustrophobic in the shuttle or the space station. I love those tight cluttered spaces because I can curl up and go to sleep. I do the space stuff because of the view. The view is the big deal. The view during the spacewalk is the best ever. The view out of the window is the next best. The Earth is bright blue, with the brown of the Sahara and the reds of Africa, or on the night side the subtle black-blue that comes from the Earth reflecting moonlight. And then there's the galaxy: the full range of colours astronomers talk about are visible to you in space. From Earth they're all a whitish yellow – you could only pick out a couple as red. In space that atmospheric distortion is removed and the stars have unique colours. The galaxy is an awesome thing to look at.

On my last flight, my biggest impression of the Earth was as the cradle of humanity. I'd look at Sudan and Iraq every day and I'd think: 'Couldn't we do this right?' I'd look down at Asia and southern Russia and China and Afghanistan, and there's no light there at all. It's like a barren planet there at night. Whereas all the coastlines are lit up – Europe, United States, Japan. The disparities on Earth geographically became a great focus and interest for me.

After a long flight – five or six months – all you're really thinking about is getting back to life on Earth. I missed seeing people, being with my family. I always dream of Earth when I'm in space, and I often dream of space when I'm on Earth. **MIKE FOALE**

Dr Mike Foale (pictured left and above) has made six space flights and has spent a total of 373.76 days in orbit. He works at Nasa training astronauts, supporting the Russian Soyuz spacecraft missions and working on Project Orion, which is intended to replace the Space Shuttle

What are...

Asteroids, comets and meteor showers

The material left over from the birth of the solar system is mainly confined to a region between the orbits of Mars and Jupiter which is known as the asteroid belt. Although asteroids orbit the Sun, they are too small to be considered planets. They range in size from large lumps of rock to objects that have diameters of around 1,000 km (600 miles).

Comets are balls of ice and dust that orbit the Sun – some take only a few years, others require millions to make a single circuit. Their orbits are invariably elliptical, bringing them very close to the Sun on occasion. Then they become visible from Earth as the Sun's heat vaporises their ice, creating a tail of dust and vapour.

Halley's comet was the first comet that was predicted to reappear in the sky at regular intervals. Sir Edmond Halley studied records of past appearances and suggested that one comet followed a similar track through the sky roughly every 76 years, appearing in 1531, 1607, and 1682. He predicted that it would reappear in 1759. It did – proving that these bodies are not just atmospheric phenomenan as previously thought, but that they orbit the Sun. The comet's next appearance is due around 28 July 2061.

Meteorites are tiny fragments of space debris which fall to the surface of a planet or moon – more than a tonne of meteorites fall to Earth each day. The friction caused by travelling through the Earth's atmosphere at several thousand metres per second heats up the meteorites and many burn up before they impact. These are known as meteors, or shooting stars. At certain times of year, a great number of meteors are visible in the night sky, and these meteor showers occur when the Earth passes through the trail of debris left by a comet as it orbits the Sun. **Robin McKie**

Omega

The astronaut's watch of choice

Ever since 1967, the Omega Speedmaster (pictured) has been the standard Apollo astronaut's watch. However, despite what they'd like you to believe, it isn't the only – or even the first – watch to have gone into space. John Glenn, the first American in space, wore a Heuer stopwatch back in 1962, and Yuri Gagarin used a Russian-made Shturmanskie chronograph. The Omega, however, does have the distinction of being the only watch to have been worn on the Moon.

A Brief History of Time in 30 seconds

More than 9 million copies of Stephen Hawking's attempt to write a popular version of the most complex subjects in science have flown off the shelves, although it's often jokingly suggested that the number of people who have actually read the book can be counted on the fingers of one hand.

Scything through the Big Bang, black holes, gravitational theory and the fundamentals of time itself, Hawking invokes the spirit of Einstein to tie it all together. Having been told by an editor that for every equation used in the book the readership would halve, Hawking picked $E=mc^2$ and ran with it, using no other equation to create such an ambitious explanation of how the universe works and to glimpse 'the mind of God'.

The book's massive success is more an example of the public's romantic pining for a flawed genius than a genuine explosion of interest in quantum mechanics (a disgraceful number of contemporary reviews act like a patronising pat on the head to Hawking), but as a summary of everything modern astrophysics has discovered, well, it's not bad. If you can get past the first chapter, that is...

The Observer **archive: historic moments in space exploration**

The first man-made satellite

(4 October 1957)

During the past week, the confused and shifting frontier between scientific fact and science fiction seems to have melted away altogether. What does the Russian satellite mean? Is it a successful scientific experiment, a military menace, or the first step to the moon? Is the 'Space Age', long familiar in fiction, now upon us in fact?

To begin with, 'Sputnik 1' (pictured) – as the Russians call their satellite – is an astonishing technical achievement, much more ambitious than the projected American satellite, and 10 times heavier. This makes it potentially 10 times as useful as a 'space laboratory' because it can carry far more measuring and recording instruments. ...

A more sobering aspect of the Russian satellite is that it must have been launched by a rocket with the performance of an intercontinental ballistic missile (ICBM). In fact, it probably was such a missile, adapted for the purpose. The satellite was launched at a height of about 300 miles and a speed of 18,000mph. The same rocket could carry a warhead to a target 5,000 miles away.

In launching a satellite, there is little room for error in the launching height, speed or direction. The Russian launching rocket must have been very accurately controlled and guided to get Sputnik 1 into an orbit at all, let alone such a successful one. The Americans have been very worried by this guidance problem, although they will certainly solve it successfully, too. The signs are, therefore, that the Russian satellite launching rocket could be guided accurately enough to New York as well.

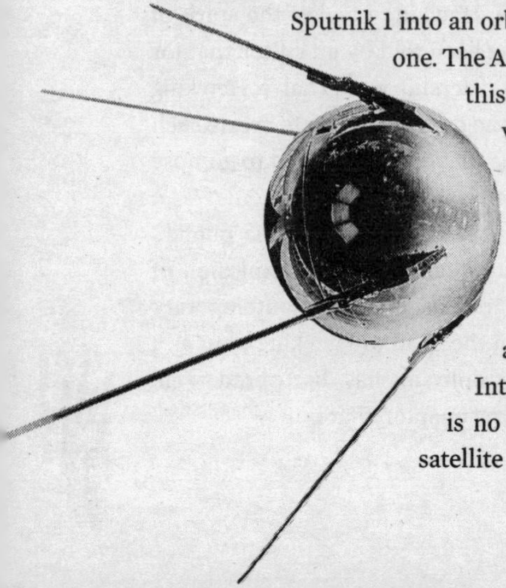

Thus, although the satellite projects are 'peaceful' contributions to the International Geophysical Year, there is no avoiding the fact that the Russian satellite is the most pointed demonstration that Mr Khrushchev means what he says in claiming to have an effective ICBM. It also seems obvious that the Russian satellite and missile programmes are intimately dovetailed. From the Soviet point of view, this is clearly the most economic way of doing things, and of making the best use of their scientists and engineers. ...

Finally, what about manned satellites and space travel? It would be rash today to echo the present Astronomer Royal's remark shortly after his appointment that 'Space travel is bunk'. But on a sober assessment, it does look very nearly bunk.

Sending up a man in a satellite also means sending up food, drink and air to keep him alive; protection from heat, cold, meteors and cosmic rays; and means of getting him safely down again. It is possible to work out the kind of equipment and rockets which would be needed, and ICBMs and Sputnik I look like Stone Age implements in comparison.

Space Fact and Fictio[n]

By JOHN DAVY, Our Scientific Correspondent

DURING the past week, the confused and shifting frontier between scientific fact and science fiction seems to have melted away altogether. What does the Russian satellite mean? Is it a successful scientific experiment, a military menace, or the first step to the moon? Is the "Space Age," long familiar in fiction, now upon us in fact?

Rocket Missiles

Towards the Moon

'Project Vanguard'

Getting it Down

John Davy, 13 October 1957

Factfile: The launch of Sputnik 1 sent the world into a frenzy. As *The Observer* reported on 6 October 1957: 'Each time the satellite circled the Earth, engineers picked up the signals – by last evening they had been picked up 15 times. In many parts of the world the signals were being received for periods of 20 minutes or so every hour and a half all yesterday. Reception was reported from United States and from Australia, Belgium, France, Holland, Sweden, Latin-American and other countries.' The BBC broadcast the 'peep-peep' signal and millions tuned in to listen. The importance of the achievement was only just being grasped a week later in this *Observer* piece, but the space race was in full swing and despite Davy's 'sober assessment', the following month the USSR sent up Laika the dog and followed this triumph with a manned mission in 1961

The visionaries: great figures from space history

Nicolaus Copernicus

(b. 19 February 1473; d. 24 May 1543)
Mathematician and astronomer

Copernicus founded modern astronomy and completely changed the way we think about the solar system with his 1543 work *De Revolutionibus Orbium Coelestium* (*On the Revolutions of the Heavenly Spheres*) which instigated the Copernican Revolution. In it, he detailed the simple discovery that had become his life's work – that all the planets, including the Earth, revolve around the Sun.

Having picked up a passion for the skies while studying astronomy at the University of Krakow, Copernicus moved around Europe for more than a decade, studying medicine and canon law, before holing up in the tower of Frauenburg Cathedral in 1519. The town suffered siege and plunder from warring Teutonic Knights, but Copernicus continued searching the stars for clues unabated, taking measurements using just his naked eye.

> *“The world had scarcely become known as round and complete in itself when it was asked to waive the tremendous privilege of being the centre of the universe.*
>
> Goethe

For the next 20 years he worked on his book, writing and rewriting, refusing to let anyone see it until it was perfect. It took a young disciple, Georg Joachim Rheticus, to finally convince him to release *De Revolutionibus* to a Nuremberg printer in 1543. Fearful that the book might insult the Church, Lutheran philosopher Andreas Osiander – asked to supervise the printing – replaced Copernicus' preface with a letter stating that the contents of the book were not intended as the truth, but merely as a method of calculating the positions of the heavenly bodies.

It was a prescient move: Copernicus' work would provoke an unparalleled oppression of science by the religious elite, and remained on the Vatican's Index of Forbidden Books for more than 250 years.

Looking up

The early astronomers

Man has been gazing at the heavens since he first stepped out of his cave. It was the Greeks, as usual, who made the first key scientific observations, with Ptolemy's *Almagest* around 150 AD. This tome laid out the geocentric view of the solar system (with the Sun and planets orbiting Earth) that would become the dominant theory for nearly 1,500 years until Copernicus published his heliocentric theory.

> “*We are all in the gutter, but some of us are looking at the stars.*
> Oscar Wilde

Ptolemy's ideas were picked up and expanded by the great Muslim scholars of Islam's golden age (700-1300 AD), who used their unique position straddling the western and eastern worlds to foment many of the mathematical advances that would become central to Copernicus', Kepler's and Galileo's Renaissance breakthroughs.

Ja'far al-Sadiq in the 8th century and Ja'far al-Balkhi in the 9th actually presaged Copernicus, both producing strong arguments for a heliocentric solar system. Al-Sadiq even predicted that the universe was expanding, something that wasn't confirmed until the Twenties. Muhammad ibn Musa, working in Baghdad, one of the great scientific centres of the time, invented the disciplines of astrophysics and celestial mechanics in the 9th century when he discovered that heavenly bodies follow the same laws of physics as Earth. Using this revelation, he found that there is a force of attraction between them, a vision of the universe echoed six centuries later by Newton.

In the 11th century, Abu al-Rayhan al-Biruni, a Persian polymath noted as one of the greatest scientists in history, applied his new experimental method (using disciplined experimentation and observation to test scientific theory) to astronomy, performing more detailed work on ibn Musa's gravitational theories as well as confirming that the Earth rotates on its axis and that the Milky Way is composed of a huge number of nebulous stars. He would later create a definitive astronomical encyclopaedia of his findings, the *Kitab al-Qanun al Mas'udi* – possibly the most important astronomical text before Copernicus' *On the Revolutions of the Celestial Spheres*.

Anatomy of a spacesuit

Space is an extremely hostile environment. If you were to step outside a spacecraft or onto a planet with little or no atmosphere and you were not wearing a spacesuit, you would become unconscious within 15 seconds because of the lack of oxygen. You would also suffer ebullism, as a reduction in pressure causes exposed organs such as skin and eyes to expand and the saliva on your tongue to boil. You would also face extreme changes in temperature – 120C in sunlight, -100C in the shade – and be exposed to various types of radiation, such as cosmic rays, and charged particles emitted from the sun. You would also be pelted by small particles of dust or rock or orbiting debris from satellites or spacecraft. A spacesuit is vital. Here's how it works...

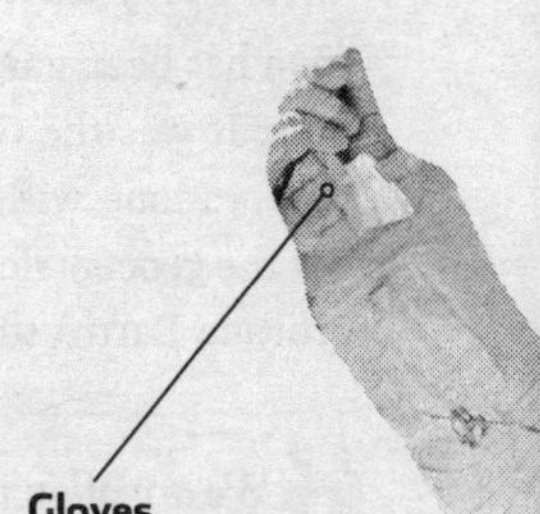

Gloves
Contain fingertip heaters and a hot pad to stop the hands from freezing

Drink bag
An in-suit drink bag contains 600g of drinking water

Maximum absorbency garment
Every astronaut must wear a maximum absorbency garment (MAG) – essentially a pair of Y-fronts that hygienically soak up any effluence with minimum discomfort

Cost
Each suit costs about $2 million (£1m) and weighs about 50kg (140kg with the backpack). There is a well-stocked wardrobe of suits available to Nasa's 120-strong astronaut corps and each Shuttle crew member is assigned three – one for training, one for the mission and a backup

Cooling
Underneath the spacesuit itself an astronaut wears a liquid cooling and ventilation garment, with water-cooling tubes running through it to regulate body temperature

Layers
The suit is approximately 0.5cm thick and made from 11 layers of material including Kevlar, coated nylon and stainless steel. These keep out both dangerous radiation and micrometeoroids (tiny rocks that shoot through space at great speeds) and provide insulation. Spacesuits offer only limited protection from the radiation of solar flares, so spacewalks are planned during periods of low solar activity

Air pressure
The spacesuit provides air pressure, acting like a protective balloon around the astronaut to prevent bodily fluids from boiling

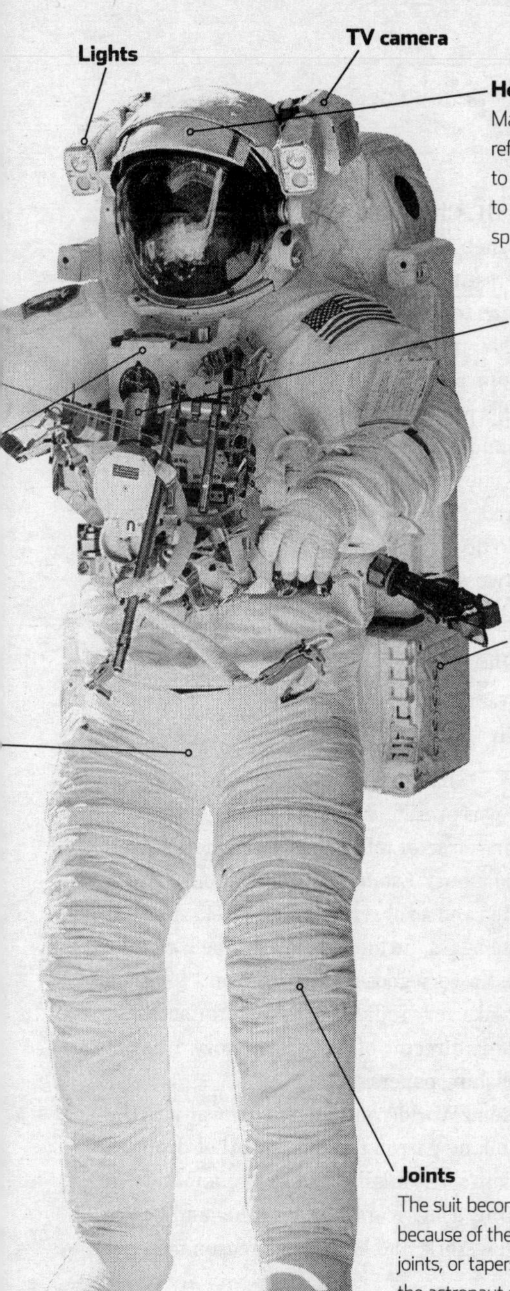

Helmet
Made from hard plastic with coverings to reflect sunlight and tinted polycarbonate to reduce glare built into the visor. Prior to a spacewalk, the inside of the visor is sprayed with an anti-fog compound

Temperature control valve
Allows heat out through fans in the backpack. The spacesuit is built to withstand temperatures of 120C in sunlight and -100C in the shade: it switches from one extreme to the other every 45 minutes as the astronaut is whizzing around in Earth's orbit. The suit is white to reflect heat

Backpack
Includes enough oxygen to last about 7 hours in space, with a 30-minute emergency supply. Spacesuits provide pure oxygen because the normal air mix – 78% nitrogen, 21% oxygen and 1% other gases – would cause dangerously low oxygen concentrations in the lungs and blood at low pressure. Oxygen is supplied either by the spacecraft via an umbilical cord or from a backpack life-support system. Lithium hydroxide canisters filter out the CO_2. Both the Shuttle and the International Space Station have breathable air mixtures that mimic our atmosphere

Joints
The suit becomes incredibly stiff in space because of the pressure difference, so special joints, or tapers, are built into the fabric to help the astronaut move around

The insider: stargazer

Patrick Moore

I had picked up a copy of GF Chambers' *The Story of the Solar System* when I was six and thought it was darned interesting. I got some ordinary binoculars and began to learn my way around the sky. I had a little star map and I made it a goal to learn one new constellation a night. The first thing I saw through a proper telescope was the Moon. I was eight, and it fascinated me. The Moon was for me, and it always has been – she's the love of my life.

Astronomy was considered a way-out subject in those days and wasn't taken very seriously. The idea of lunar travel was regarded as wild science fiction. I had two slices of luck. A family friend was a member of the British Astronomical Association and he recommended me as a member when I was 11 years old – I was the youngest at that time. I went to London and shook hands with the Astronomer Royal. Fifty years later to the day, I was president.

> *"The eternal mystery of the world is its comprehensibility.*
> Albert Einstein

Then I acquired a little 3in refractor telescope. Near where I lived in East Grinstead was the Hanbury Estate, and Mr Hanbury had a small observatory in his garden and an observer called WS Franks – at 4ft 9in and with a long white beard, he looked exactly like a gnome. He was an amazing man and a very good astronomer and took me on as his assistant. Then Franks very sadly died in a motor accident and I, at the age of 14, became director of the observatory. I began mapping the Moon and publishing papers.

At the outbreak of the Second World War I fiddled my way into the RAF and was very close to taking part in the missions that dropped bombs on Wernher von Braun's V-2 missile site in Peenemünde in 1943. I'm glad I didn't do it. Only a few years later Wernher and I were having dinner together in New York, and he was the reason man got to the Moon.

After the war I wrote *A Guide to the Moon* and then *A Guide to the Planets* for a popular audience, and the BBC asked me to do the television programme *The Sky at Night*. It's been on every month since, and I've missed only one episode in all that time – in 2004, when I ate the wrong kind of goose egg. If I could find that bird I'd wring its neck.

In 1958 I got a letter from the Russians asking: 'Can you send us all the maps of the Moon's edge that you haven't published?' I sent it to them. Then they sent a 'bird' round it. The International Astronomical Union has always been entirely international – even at the height of the Cold War the president was American and the vice president Russian. Astronomy has been an arena of cooperation, but space has always had military connotations, and it still does.

I was on the Nasa Moon committee and provided maps for them. I know all the astronauts very well. When Neil and Buzz were going down to land I did the commentary for the BBC, and I knew there was no provision for rescue. If there had been a faulty landing, they would have been stranded. So when I heard Neil's voice coming through, saying: 'The Eagle has landed', I felt a surge of relief. Then when they took off to come back they had one ascent engine which had to work first time or they would have been stuck, and fortunately it did. I remember them saying that the greatest phenomenon was seeing the Earth a quarter of a million miles away.

The most amazing thing I've ever seen is a total eclipse of the Sun. I've seen seven. The last one occurred when I was in Cornwall, but I was under cloud when it happened. Chance plays a big part, and you have to accept it. We were in the Philippine Islands five years ago for another and it was raining cats and dogs, and then suddenly we had 40 seconds of clear sky just as totality happened. **Patrick Moore**

Sir Patrick Moore is presenter of The Sky At Night, *the longest-running television series (with the same presenter) in the world, and has done more than anyone else to raise the profile of astronomy for the British public. He is also a virtuoso on the xylophone*

The sky at night

Patrick Moore's guide to stargazing

Getting to know the night skies is much easier than you would think, even with the naked eye or a pair of binoculars. There are only a few thousand stars visible to the naked eye, and the patterns never change. It is only the planets of the solar system that shift around. Binoculars help a bit. You can get a reasonable telescope now for under £100, a small refractor. But for £400 you can get a Meade or a Celestron, which will get you around 150 magnification and last you a lifetime.

The Orion Nebula

Orion or the Hunter is the first of our two guiding lights to the night sky, along with Ursa Major. It disappears for part of the summer but is always visible in the winter, and it's a spectacular bright 'X' of stars with a belt across the middle.

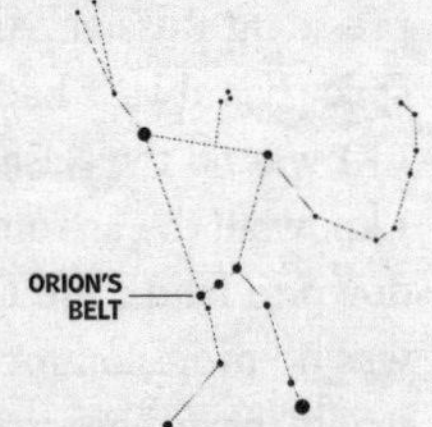

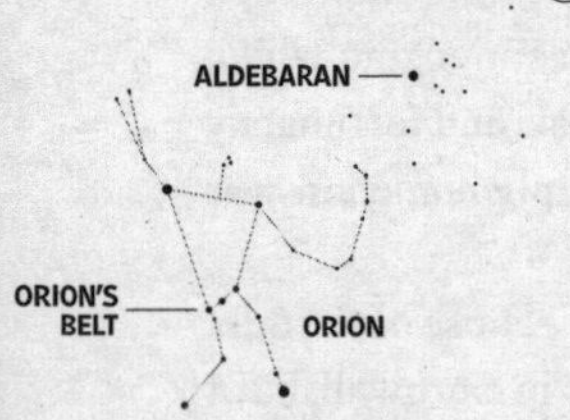

The Pleiades

Follow the line of the Orion belt upwards and you come to a bright red star called Aldebaran – this is in fact a star cluster of the Hyades, a kind of 'V' shape. Further on still are the seven sisters, or the Pleiades: a lovely star cluster 400 light years away. See how many stars you can see in the Pleiades with the naked eye. Binoculars show dozens, a small telescope hundreds.

Sirius

Follow Orion's Belt downward and you can see Sirius, the brightest star in the sky.

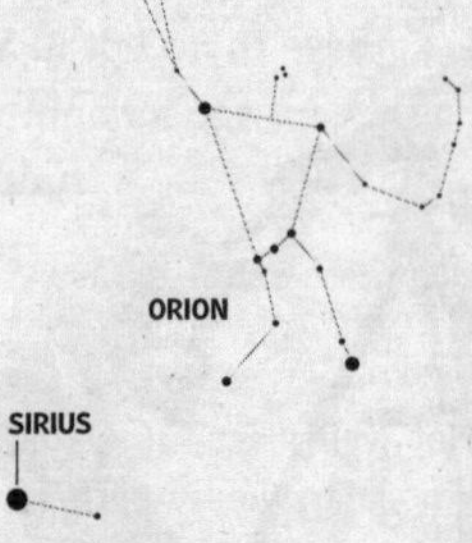

Ursa Major (the Great Bear or Plough)

Seven famous stars make up the Plough pattern. This never sets over any part of Britain. Look at the second star and you'll see it's a wonderful double star – a Mizar.

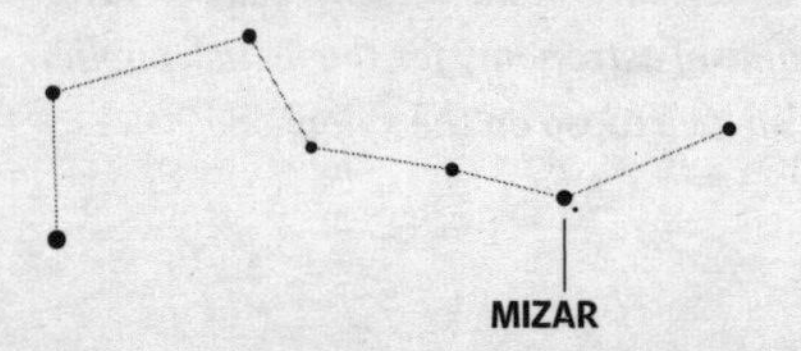

Andromeda

Look for the square of the Pegasus constellation, and just above it is the Andromeda Nebula spiral galaxy, one of the most distant objects visible to the naked eye at 2 million light years away.

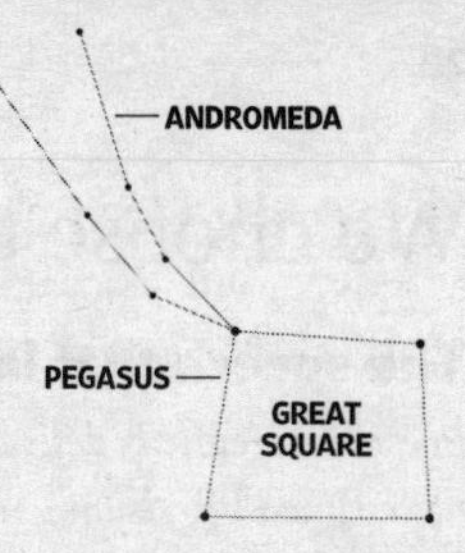

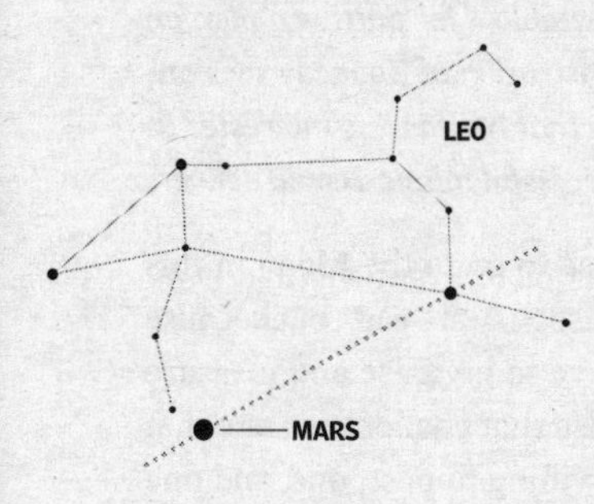

Mars

This winter Mars will be in the constellation of Leo, visible to the eye as a bright red star. With a small telescope you'll be able to see the dark markings and the white polar caps.

The Milky Way

The Via Lactea – or Milk of the Gods, as the Greeks called it – is always spectacular. You can see many stars all crammed in behind each other.

The Geminids

Between 7 and 14 December 2007 the Geminids are visible, bright meteor showers, and the Moon's out of the way, so it could be quite spectacular. It's cometary debris, a trail of dust that burns up in the Earth's atmosphere.

Venus

Brilliant in the morning sky in the late autumn. You want to see it rise just before the Sun does, and you can see it low in the sky.

The Sun

It's fascinating, but never look straight at it. Instead project an image by holding up a piece of card with a pinhole in it and looking at a piece of card behind, on which will be a projected image with all of its sunspots and faculae on view.

Tuttle's comet

Requires a telescope, but it'll be near the pole star at the end of December.

Saturn

Not well placed until the summer, but then it's a marvellous sight. With binoculars you can just see something strange about the shape; with a small telescope you can see the rings, which is a most extraordinary sight.

We choose to go to the Moon

The speech that launched a thousand rockets

President Kennedy delivered a rousing speech in Houston, Texas in which he outlined his vision – and crucially a timetable – for putting a man on the Moon. The speech was seen as a demonstration of Kennedy's visionary leadership, but it has since been shown that he was less interested in space than in the political advantages a successful mission could deliver.

We choose to go to the Moon. We choose to go to the Moon in this decade and do the other things, not because they are easy, but because they are hard, because that goal will serve to organise and measure the best of our energies and skills, because that challenge is one that we are willing to accept, one we are unwilling to postpone, and one which we intend to win, and the others, too. ...

But if I were to say, my fellow citizens, that we shall send to the Moon, 240,000 miles away from the control station in Houston, a giant rocket more than 300ft tall, the length of this football field, made of new metal alloys, some of which have not yet been invented, capable of standing heat and stresses several times more than have ever been experienced, fitted together with a precision better than the finest watch, carrying all the equipment needed for propulsion, guidance, control, communications, food and survival, on an untried mission, to an unknown celestial body, and then return it safely to Earth, re-entering the atmosphere at speeds of over 25,000 miles per hour, causing heat about half that of the temperature of the Sun – almost as hot as it is here today – and do all this, and do it right, and do it first before this decade is out – then we must be bold. ...

Many years ago the great British explorer George Mallory, who was to die on Mount Everest, was asked why did he want to climb it. He said, 'Because it is there.' Well, space is there, and we're going to climb it, and the Moon and the planets are there, and new hopes for knowledge and peace are there. And therefore as we set sail we ask God's blessing on the most hazardous and dangerous and greatest adventure on which man has ever embarked.

John F Kennedy, Rice Stadium, 12 September 1962

What is...

A light year

On Earth we use kilometres and miles to measure distances – London to New York is 5,567km (3,459 miles). In space, the closest star to Earth besides the Sun, Proxima Centauri, is 38,000,000,000,000km (24,000,000,000,000 miles) away. Because these distances are so vast, the speed of light is used as a measurement. Light travels at 300,000km (186,000 miles) per second and the most common unit is called a light year – the distance that light can travel in one Earth year (365 days). It takes light 365 days to travel 9,460,000,000,000km (5,880,000,000,000 miles). So the distance from Earth to Proxima Centauri more easily translates into approximately four light years.

The light from a star 1 million light years away has travelled at the speed of light to reach us. So it has taken 1m years to get to Earth and we are seeing what the star looked like 1m years ago, not what it would really look like today if we were able to view that star up close. The entire night sky would look very different if it weren't for this delay. Our Sun is eight or so light minutes away.

Light years are also combined into larger units known as parsecs: one parsec is equal to 3.26 light years or 30.9 trillion km (19.2 trillion miles).

Five classic TV shows about space

***The Jetsons* (1962-1963)** The Flintstones in the future

***Doctor Who* (1963-2007)** A mad doctor abducts a girl for time and space travel adventures

***Mork and Mindy* (1978-1982)** An alien moves in with a woman and wackiness ensues

***Buck Rogers in the 25th Century* (1979-1981)** An astronaut is frozen in time and wakes up in a future made of spandex

***The Hitchhiker's Guide To The Galaxy* (1981)** Definitive screen version of the classic book

The visionaries: great figures from space history

Johannes Kepler

(b. 27 December 1571; d. 15 November 1630)
Mathematician and astronomer

Johannes Kepler, a poor, sickly boy from Weil der Stadt, near Stuttgart, would go on to formulate some of the most important theories in astronomy, and turn it from an abstract, liberal subject into a firmly scientific discipline. A massive influence on both Isaac Newton and Galileo, his *Astronomia Nova* (1609) gave us the laws of planetary motion, making him the first to describe the planets' elliptical orbits – the first recorded 'natural laws', universal, verifiable and precise.

> *The treasures hidden in the heavens [are] so rich, precisely in order that the human mind shall never be lacking in fresh nourishment.*
> Johannes Kepler

As a student, Kepler became a disciple of Copernicus and studied under the great astronomer Tycho Brahe in Prague before becoming imperial mathematician of the Holy Roman Empire – the most prestigious mathematics position in Europe. It was while in this post that he published his 1604 breakthrough *Astronomia pars Optica*, in which he invented modern optics and laid the foundations for the invention of the telescope.

After these impressive discoveries, he went on to suggest that the tides are caused by the Moon's gravitational pull (Galileo dismissed this as 'useless fiction'). He detailed how the Sun rotates around its own axis, and while describing Jupiter's moons he coined the word 'satellite'. He even used his knowledge of the movements of Jupiter, Saturn and Mars to calculate that, if Bible records are correct, Jesus was born six years earlier than previously thought.

Kepler remained religious to the end, glimpsing God in the cosmos: 'I had the intention of becoming a theologian, but now I see God is, by my endeavours, also glorified in astronomy, for "the heavens declare the glory of God".'

Universal laws

The Outer Space Treaty and other agreements

Almost as soon as mankind ventured into space, we couldn't resist the urge to draw up a complex treaty to regulate its use and exploration. Even the US and Russia, locked in the Cold War space race, sought to work together to make sure space exploration remained a noble enterprise benefiting all humanity rather than a few greedy superpowers. The first treaty signed was the clumsily entitled Declaration of Legal Principles Governing the Activities of States in the Exploration and Use of Outer Space, created in 1962. It was subsequently polished and expanded into 1967's Outer Space Treaty, which has now been signed by more than 120 countries, although not all have ratified it yet.

The treaty was followed by agreements concerning the rescue of astronauts and the registration of objects launched into outer space, and finally by the Moon Agreement of 1979. All signatories to this latter document must guarantee that any natural resources discovered on the Moon or any other celestial body become the property of all mankind, subject to an international regime governing their exploitation. This was met with consternation from the major space powers, and was not ratified by any nation actually undertaking manned space flight.

Five key points of the Outer Space Treaty

1 The exploration and use of outer space shall be carried out for the benefit and in the interests of all countries, and shall be the province of all mankind.

2 Outer space is not subject to national appropriation by claim of sovereignty, by means of use or occupation, or by any other means.

3 States shall not place nuclear weapons or other weapons of mass destruction in orbit or on celestial bodies.

4 Astronauts shall be regarded as the envoys of mankind.

5 States shall be liable for damage caused by their space objects.

Science fiction or science fact?

The truth about six depictions of space

1 *Star Trek* (1966-2005)

Is teleportation possible?

Yes (well, sort of). Scientists in the US and Austria have developed a way to teleport an atom's 'quantum state' to another atom using quantum physics so complex it'll make your brain ache. The technology could enable the invention of super-fast quantum computers – however, it's unlikely that anything bigger than an atom will benefit from such a breakthrough.

2 *2001: A Space Odyssey* (1968)

If a person was exposed to space unprotected, shouldn't he or she explode or at least boil rather than just suffocate and drift away as Dr Dave Bowman, the spacecraft's commander does in the film?

No. A human could actually survive for a few minutes in space and, if they were pulled back into a pressurised spacecraft after 30 seconds or so, would actually survive unscathed. This actually happened in 1965, when a Nasa astronaut was put in a vacuum chamber with a damaged suit. He remained conscious for 14 seconds before the chamber was quickly repressurised, and reported that he could feel and hear the air leaking out, with the saliva on his tongue beginning to boil.

3 *Star Wars* (1977)

Could TIE (twin ion engine) fighters exist?

Yes. Nasa has successfully tested ion propulsion on several unmanned spacecraft, such as Deep Space 1. It works by firing xenon ions out the back of a spacecraft, propelling the ship forward. Despite the fact that the ions push on the spacecraft with about the force of a piece of paper resting on your hand, these engines could attain speeds 10 times higher than a chemical engine, and are cheaper and longer lasting, so ideally suited to travelling very long distances through space. They wouldn't, however, be well suited to propelling fighters, as acceleration is very slow.

4 *Alien* (1979)

In space, can anyone hear you scream?

No. Sound waves cannot travel in a vacuum, and space is the closest thing to a vacuum that we know (there are still a few hydrogen atoms for every cubic metre). Therefore any event, from a star exploding to a TIE fighter screaming past, would happen in total silence.

5 *Armageddon* (1998)

Could we really land a man on an asteroid?

Yes, potentially. Nasa already has plans in place to launch a manned flight to one of our local asteroids (near-Earth asteroids, or NEAs), seeing it as a technological stepping stone to an eventual manned mission to Mars. At the moment this mission would be for purely scientific reasons – there are no plans to nuke an asteroid just yet.

6 *Sunshine* (2007)

Could the Sun really die in 50 years?

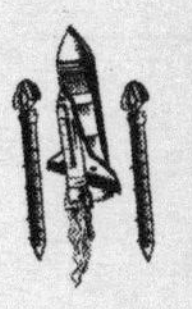

Theoretically, perhaps. Officially the Sun is enjoying a quiet middle age and is expected to last another 5 billion years – however Brian Cox, a physicist who worked with the filmmakers to keep the movie's science respectable, came up with a theory to explain how the Sun could be in its last throes of life by 2057. The answer came with Q balls, hypothetical particles that eat through normal matter, which physicists are only just beginning to understand. If one of these became lodged in the Sun (an incredibly unlikely event), the star's neutrons and protons would be ripped apart, effectively killing it. If this happened, could we save ourselves by sending a bomb the size of Manhattan into the Sun? Well, no. It'd be the equivalent of trying to set fire to Mount Everest with a match.

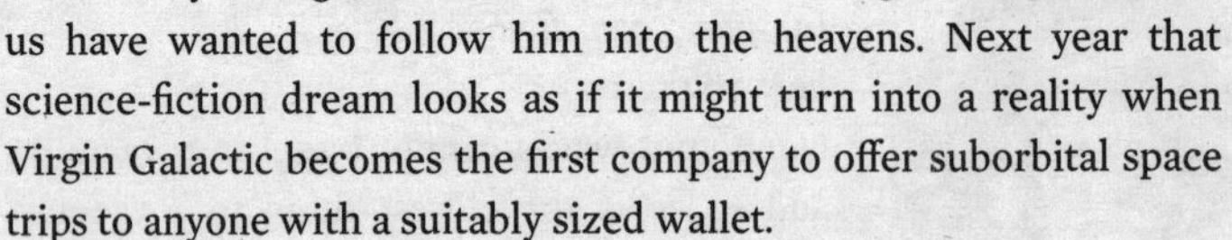

Space tourism

The holiday of a lifetime

Ever since Yuri Gagarin was blasted into space in what was little more than an overgrown tin can 46 years ago, the more adventurous among us have wanted to follow him into the heavens. Next year that science-fiction dream looks as if it might turn into a reality when Virgin Galactic becomes the first company to offer suborbital space trips to anyone with a suitably sized wallet.

With the FAA predicting space tourism to become a £350 million-a-year industry by 2021, Virgin Galactic's boss Richard Branson (pictured) isn't the only one setting his sights on the stars. Jim Benson, of Benson Space, has created the Dream Chaser, which he hopes will be able to offer flights for as little as £24,500 by 2014, and there is a wealth of companies investing in technology that could offer us the chance to go further and for longer, with the possibility of space hotels and lunar trips by the end of the next decade.

However, space tourism is a risky business. Companies have already acknowledged that they do not have the same budget, or indeed the same need, to keep the risks as low as Nasa does. For Nasa, a fatality spells a massive loss of prestige and the possible end of the programme; private firms will state the risk (thought to be a 1 in 50 chance of death; the average plane flight has a risk of about 1 in 10 million) and allow people to make up their own minds. Despite these potential hazards, it won't be long before the man on the street becomes the man on the Moon.

The X Prize

The modern 'second space race' to become the first company to offer private trips into space was launched with the formation of the X Prize competition in 1996. It promised a $10m (£4.9m) payout to the first non-governmental organisation to launch a reusable spacecraft that could fly into space and back twice within two weeks, luring the private sector into a traditionally government-run industry. It was won by the Tier One project's SpaceShipOne craft, designed by Burt Rutan and funded by Microsoft's Paul Allen in 2004.

The spaceship

Virgin Galactic will use an adapted version of Burt Rutan's X Prize-winning SpaceShipOne – imaginatively named SpaceShipTwo – to launch up to six passengers and two pilots into space. To get up there, the craft will piggyback onto Rutan's White Knight Two rocket before being set free to float around 110km up and then glide back to its Norman Foster-designed spaceport in New Mexico (one is also planned for Sweden, positioned under the Aurora Borealis).

For a hefty £107,000 (Virgin hopes to slash this cost to around £42,000 after a few years), passengers will receive three days' training followed by a 2.5-hour flight. For six minutes of the journey they will be able to take off their seatbelts and float in zero gravity, wearing spacesuits by Louis Vuitton and viewing Earth and the star-filled heavens from the windows of the Philippe Starck-designed interior.

But all this hasn't stopped its detractors. William Shatner, on being offered a free seat on the maiden voyage, offered the succinct reply: 'I'm interested in man's march into the unknown, but to vomit in space is not my idea of a good time. Neither is a fiery crash with the vomit hovering over me.'

What's next?

Lunar rover The X Prize Foundation has offered a $30m (£14.7m) prize to the first non-governmental organisation to land a rover on the Moon

Orbit A $50m (£24.5m) prize will be awarded to whoever can build the first private orbiting vessel, offering tourists a much longer time in zero gravity

Space hotel Hilton, Virgin and British Airways are considering it; the Space Island Group is planning to house up to 20,000 people on their 'space island' by 2020

Space ferry Bigelow Aerospace is offering $50m to the first company to design and build a reusable spacecraft that could ferry customers to their Nautilus space station

The Moon Space Adventures is currently working on the possibility of allowing commercial passengers to orbit the Moon. The cost at first is likely to be around $100m (£49m)

Out of this world

A brief history of space tourism

After the break-up of the Soviet Union, the Russian Space Agency found itself strapped for cash at a time when the International Space Station (ISS), the conception and building of which was in no small way down to the Russians, was eating up funds. To plug this hole, the government teamed up with US-based company Space Adventures to offer civilians the chance to spend time on board the ISS. Nasa originally objected, arguing that civilians flying with little training and no language skills would endanger the mission and crew, but after the Russians persuaded them that the tourists would receive months of training and would be forced to sign a waiver stating that their heirs couldn't sue Nasa and would pay for any breakages, Nasa relented, and the first tourist was sent up in 2001. Here are the five brave (and rich) souls who have paid to go into space...

Dennis Tito (pictured) (28 April-6 May 2001)

Tito, the first space tourist, prefers to be called an 'independent researcher', as the millionaire New Yorker and former Nasa scientist performed several scientific experiments while in orbit. He did, however, have to pay a reported $20 million (£9.8m) for the privilege.

Mark Shuttleworth (25 April-5 May 2002)

The South African internet tycoon made his fortune by selling an internet security firm he had started in his mother's basement for $500m (£246m). He paid $20m to become the first African in space, and while up there had a conversation with Nelson Mandela and also turned down a 14-year-old South African girl who asked if he would marry her.

Gregory Olsen (1-11 October 2005)
Olsen is another private astronaut who dislikes the term 'space tourist'. A physics professor who made his fortune through the development of sensitive infrared cameras (and whose main customer is Nasa), he used the flight as an opportunity to grow crystals that might be used in his cameras.

Anousheh Ansari (18-29 September 2006)
The Iranian-American became the first female Muslim and the first Iranian in space when she gave the Russians a chunk of her family's telecommunications millions for the pleasure of a space flight. She and her brother-in-law had made a large donation to the X Prize in 2004, which was renamed the Ansari X Prize in their honour.

Charles Simonyi (7-21 April 2007)
Simonyi is a Hungarian computer-software executive who amassed a $1 billion fortune through overseeing the creation of Microsoft Office in the Nineties. He has been dating Martha Stewart, the entrepreneurial TV chef, since February 2007.

What is...

A supernova

As a star's fuel runs out and its nuclear-fusion reactions stop, the star's gravity pulls in material, compressing the core, which heats up and explodes. These stellar explosions cause a burst of radiation that may briefly outshine its entire host galaxy before fading from view over several weeks or months. During this short interval, the supernova radiates as much energy as the Sun would emit over 10 billion years and sends out a shockwave that sweeps up an expanding shell of gas and dust called a supernova remnant, which can turn into a black hole. On average, supernovae occur about once every 50 years in a galaxy the size of the Milky Way. **Robin McKie**

The Observer archive: historic moments in space exploration

The first man in space

(12 April 1961)

Spaceman Yuri Gagarin, flanked by four members of the Soviet Academy of Sciences, gave his first press conference today, revealing barely anything about his spaceship but telling us a good deal about the pleasure and thrill of being inside.

The young airman looked extremely fit and resplendent in his new medals and decorations. He told us he now wanted to go to Venus and Mars and to make a serious business of 'conquering space'. ... Among the few points Gagarin was willing to tell us about his spaceship was that it was designed to encircle the earth and could not travel to the moon, but special spaceships were being created for flights to the moon. ...

The biologist Academician Sissakayan said space pilots needed exceptional stamina and 'the iron will inculcated by a great Leninist Communist Party'. In an article in the Moscow *Literary Journal* today, Dr Parin said that the experiment was medically such a success, and Gagarin showed himself so fit and alert, that scientists now conclude that a space pilot can be trained to operate a spaceship himself instead of being just a passive passenger.

The well-known Soviet physicist Mr Feodorov also spoke, but on politics, not physics. He said Russia gladly placed the latest scientific achievement at the disposal of human progress, and made no special claim on outer space. But his secrecy about everything concerning the sputnik, and the ban on knowing where it is, suggested that this sharing is not for today.

Nora Beloff, 16 April 1961

'Macmillan more wicked than Hitler'

—RUSSELL

BERTRAND RUSSELL said yesterday: "We used to call Hitler wicked for killing off the Jews, but Kennedy and Macmillan are much more wicked than Hitler."

He told Midland members of the Youth Campaign for Nuclear Disarmament in Birmingham: "We cannot obey the murderers. They are wicked. They are abominable. They are the wickedest people who have ever lived in the history of man and it is our duty to do what we can against them.

"This idea of weapons of mass extermination is utterly horrible and is something which no one with one spark of humanity can tolerate. I will not pretend to obey a government which is organising a mass massacre of mankind. I will do everything I can to oppose the Government in every way which I feel will be fruitful. I exhort you to do the same."

'Massive ignorance'

The ignorance of important public men on the question of nuclear warfare was "utterly astounding" to those who had made an impartial study of the subject. "From important public men this ...

Gagarin guards his spaceship secrets

Vostok can be used again

From NORA BELOFF

MOSCOW, April 15

SPACEMAN Yuri Gagarin, flanked by four members of the Soviet Academy of Sciences, gave his first Press conference to-day revealing barely anything about his spaceship, but telling us a good deal about the pleasure and thrill of being inside.

The young airman looked extremely fit and resplendent in his new medals and decorations. He told us he now wanted to go to Venus and Mars and to make a serious business of "conquering space."

The earth's surface, Major Gagarin said, looks from a sputnik rather the same as it looks from a jet plane.

But there was no answer to questions about whether reconnaissance photographs can be taken from it. Major Gagarin was only willing to say there were no cameras aboard.

Among the few points Gagarin was willing to tell us about his spaceship was, first, that it was designed to encircle the earth and could not travel to the moon ...

Mr. Feodorov also spoke, but on politics, not physics. He said Russia gladly placed the latest scientific achievement at the disposal of human progress, and made no special claim on outer space. But his secrecy about everything concerning the sputnik and the ban on knowing where it is, suggested that this sharing is not for to-day.

He also said it was a scandal that while we were conquering space, men were still being exploited. He noted it as symbolic that Gagarin had flown over the Congo. The connection between Soviet space travel and African freedom has already been the theme of a number of articles and cartoons.

'Noise ...

Factfile: During his flight, Gagarin famously whistled the patriotic tune 'The Motherland Hears', written by Dmitri Shostakovich in 1951. The first lines are: 'The Motherland hears, the Motherland knows / Where her son flies in the sky'. On landing, he became an instant worldwide celebrity

Top 10 songs about space

'Sun turnin' 'round with graceful motion / We're setting off with soft explosion / Bound for a star with fiery oceans'
'2000 Light Years From Home' by the Rolling Stones, 1967

'This is Major Tom to Ground Control / I'm stepping through the door / And I'm floating in a most peculiar way'
'Space Oddity' by David Bowie, 1969

'And all this science I don't understand / It's just my job, five days a week / A rocket man, a rocket man'
'Rocket Man' by Elton John, 1972

'A spaceman came travelling on his ship from afar / 'Twas light years of time since his mission did start'
'A Spaceman Came Travelling' by Chris De Burgh, 1975

'We're moving now to come in for our landing / here Pluto / all of you who are in group A send you over to the pludatarium to get plutotised'
'A Funky Space Reincarnation' by Marvin Gaye, 1978

'I'm gonna send him to outer space to find another race / I'll take your brain to another dimension / Pay close attention'
'Out of Space' by the Prodigy, 1992

'If you believed they put a man on the Moon / man on the Moon / If you believe there's nothing up my sleeve / Then nothing is cool'
'Man on the Moon' by REM, 1993

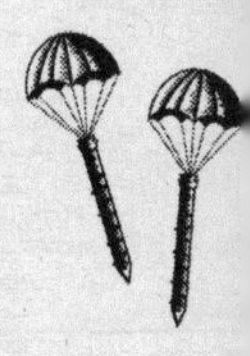

'T-minus 60 seconds and counting / Arm light on / Switching command 2 internal / Missile and new count in sync? / Affirmative'
'Space' by Prince, 1994

'Television takes control / Decimation / Different races fall / Electronic information tampers with your soul'
'Spaceman' by Babylon Zoo, 1996

'If you want to battle you're in denial / Coming from Uranus to check my style / Go ahead, put my rhymes on trial / Cast you off into exile'
'Intergalactic' by the Beastie Boys, 1998

Edwin Hubble

(b. 20 November 1889; d. 28 September 1953)
Astronomer

Edwin Powell Hubble was responsible for expanding our understanding of the universe and proving that it was far larger than we had thought. Born in the Midwestern corn belt, Hubble studied mathematics and astronomy at the University of Chicago before winning a Rhodes scholarship to study law at Oxford.

From 1919 he worked with the 100-inch Hooker telescope at the Mount Wilson Observatory in Southern California, the best in the world at that time. Through patience, careful documentation and photographs taken over six years, Hubble made an astonishing breakthrough. It had been believed that the limits of the universe were those of our home galaxy, the Milky Way, but in 1924 Hubble measured the distance to the Andromeda Nebula. Hubble showed that it is about 100,000 times as far away as the nearest stars and therefore must be a separate galaxy, comparable in size to the Milky Way. In 1929 he followed up this revelation with the theory that these separate galaxies are travelling away from us at a speed proportional to their distance. Hubble's constant, as the theory was called, coupled with Einstein's 1915 theory of general relativity, spawned the science of cosmology – the notion that the universe is expanding outwards.

> “*Equipped with his five senses, man explores the universe around him and calls the adventure Science.*
> Edwin Hubble

During the Second World War, Hubble headed US research into ballistics, and after the war he travelled and lectured, while also lobbying for astronomy to be recognised as part of the study of physics. The Nobel committee finally acceded following Hubble's death in 1953. Since 1990 a telescope bearing Hubble's name has been orbiting the Earth.

What is...

The Big Bang

The Big Bang is the best theory we have to explain how the universe came into existence. It all began with a 'singularity', a sort of infinitely small, infinitely hot, infinitely dense 'something' (there really is no other way to describe it) containing all the matter in the Universe, which suddenly began to expand around 15 billion years ago. Rather than a giant explosion, the Big Bang is best described as a balloon inflating from something so tiny we couldn't begin to comprehend its proportions to something the size of our Universe, and outside of this balloon is literally nothing – no space, no matter, no light.

> *In the beginning the universe was created. This has made a lot of people very angry and been widely regarded as a bad move.*
>
> Douglas Adams

The time scales involved are also incredible: it took just one second for the singularity to expand and cool from trillions and trillions of degrees Celsius down to a few billion, and after three minutes it was down to 1bn – cool enough for the protons and neutrons flying about this primordial soup to synthesise and create helium and hydrogen nuclei, elemental building blocks from which all other elements would eventually form. After around 30 minutes the Big Bang was over – it takes longer to cook a roast dinner than it took for the entire universe to burst into existence.

Over the next 300,000 years the universe continued to expand and cool, eventually reaching a temperature at which the helium nuclei could absorb electrons creating the first atoms. A billion years later these atoms were being brought together by gravity, forming giant gas clouds, which would eventually coalesce into galaxies, and smaller gas clouds, which would become stars. The theory was proved to be sound in 1965, when Arno Penzias and Robert Wilson discovered cosmic microwave background radiation (CMB). This background radiation is a relic left over from the Big Bang, unleashed when the universe was just 380,000 years old, and is familiar to us as the static noise we get from a detuned television or radio.

Brits in space

How our space programme failed to take off

In terms of the now truly international space race, it was always clear that the main battle would be between the US and Russia, which sprinted into an early lead. It was even predictable that France and Germany would happily jog along behind, and that the resurgent China, India and Japan would mount a late surge. What nobody predicted as the Second World War drew to a close was that the UK, one of the world's great scientific powers famed for its engineering prowess, would stumble along, bumping into every hurdle, before eventually falling flat on its face.

> "*There is no way back into the past; the choice, as Wells once said, is the universe or nothing.*
>
> Arthur C Clarke

It all could have been so different. The British Interplanetary Society had designed a theoretical Moon rocket by 1937 which, after a redesign in 1949 to incorporate new technology, successfully predicted many of the components that would go into the Apollo 11 mission in 1969. The Fifties started brightly, as Britain's desire for a rocket to deliver their new-fangled atomic bombs inevitably led scientists to look further upwards. However, money soon proved to be a problem, and despite the success of the Black Knight project, which achieved a then world-record altitude of 564km in September 1958, the British space programme's achievements were all either forgotten or incorporated into Europa, the grander European programme.

Britain spent the Sixties working with the six other European nations on this new project; however, 1970 saw its third and final failed launch, and Britain withdrew from the programme. The next year gave us a surprise success when a campaign for the funding of a small home-grown space programme, run by the Royal Aircraft Establishment throughout the Sixties, paid off – and for a paltry £9 million (the Apollo programme had cost the US some $240 billion) the Black Arrow space launcher (pictured), using the technology developed for Black Knight, launched a prototype satellite, Prospero, into space, making us only the sixth country to have performed the feat.

However, almost as soon as Prospero reached space, the government put a block on any further funding. Advised by scientists from the Royal Astronomical Society, they believed no real commercial or scientific gain could be wrought from a space programme, and so it wasn't worth the cost. This allowed the French, who saw the potential of satellite telecommunications more clearly, to quickly gain a foothold in the nascent commercial satellite-launch market with the Paris-based Ariane launcher project. Now the British stake in space is restricted to building the satellites shot into space largely by this launcher – a field in which Surrey Satellite Technology, based at the University of Surrey, is a major player.

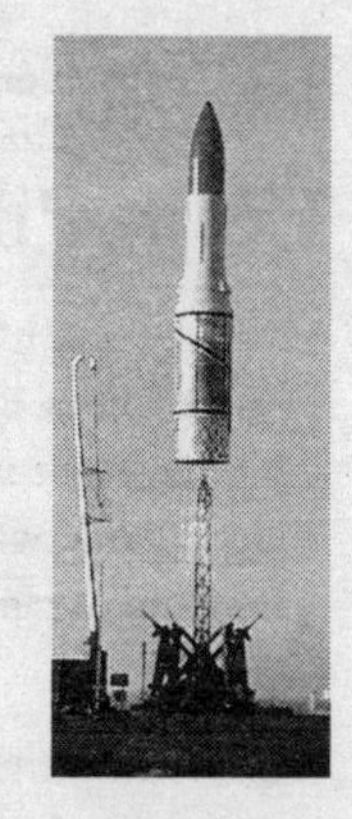

Over the years, British scientists and astronauts have been forced to look abroad. The European Space Agency (ESA) is littered with British workers, and three of the British-born astronauts to have gone into space are either fully naturalised or dual-nationality Americans. The fourth, Helen Sharman, was sent up privately with no government funding. Even Beagle 2's failure on Mars was largely due to a complete lack of public funding, forcing Professor Colin Pillinger to look to private sponsorship and forcing tight deadlines on what became a low-budget experiment. However, the future looks brighter for British space travel, as ministers recently declared that they would be interested in working with ESA and Nasa with a view to getting Britons on the Moon, and perhaps on Mars, within 20 years. But as history suggests, whether this ever will happen is a different story.

Five moments in British space history

September 1958 Black Knight rocket reaches a record 564km altitude

5 June 1961 The Blue Streak rocket is successfully launched

28 October 1971 Prototype satellite Prospero goes into a polar orbit

18 May 1991 Helen Sharman becomes the first Briton in space

December 2003 Beagle 2 fails to phone home after landing on Mars

The insider: planetary scientist

Colin Pillinger

My first encounter with space was the radio series *Journey into Space* in 1954, about Britain being the first to land on the Moon. I was 14 when Sputnik went up in 1957. Bernard Lovell, who tracked it at Jodrell Bank, was an old boy from my school, Kingswood Grammar – the kind of place they sent missionaries to convert the locals in the 18th century, so Lovell was big news.

> *A little setback like a lost lander should not discourage visionaries.*
> Colin Pillinger

In 1968 I was recruited to analyse samples of lunar rock for the Apollo Program and look for signs of life. I was doing a chemistry PhD in Swansea, and I knew how to run an instrument they needed called a mass spectrometer. I was unbelievably chuffed. Twelve astronauts walked on the surface of the Moon and did my fieldwork for me. Then I went to pick up these samples from a guy in London. It was surreal: I was carrying around 105 grams of lunar soil that two months ago was up there. It took us all of 20 minutes to realise that there wasn't any life on the Moon, but by then I was hooked.

I worked on analysing meteorites that landed on Earth, and we found that some seemed to come from Mars and that there was strong evidence of biology in one rock. We wrote: 'We have found indigenous organic matter in Martian meteorites and the implications are obvious.' Then in 1996 a Martian rock was discovered containing a nanoscopic fossil. We couldn't prove that the fossil hadn't entered the rock on Earth, so when I heard that the European Space Agency was sending an orbiter to Mars I went to see them in the hope that we could repeat the experiment on the planet to avoid the risk of contamination. After two seconds' thought they said: 'There's no money for it.'

My wife came up with the name Beagle 2 after Darwin's ship the Beagle, and we solicited everyone in the UK who might want to be involved: universities, companies, the government, and even Blur and Damien Hirst got involved. The mission appealed to a different audience, people who wouldn't think of reading a space story. We appeared in *Horse and Hound* and the *NME*. Everyone wanted to come and talk to me about the mission.

Going to Mars is bloody tough. Two-thirds of all missions disappear. The Moon is 250,000 miles away; in 2003 Mars was 35 million miles away, but for complicated reasons we had to travel 250m miles to get there. Beagle 2 was a 66cm-diameter pocket watch crammed with testing equipment, and once it was dropped from the orbiter we had to get it to slow from 12,500mph using a heat shield and two parachutes. Then before it hit the ground at around 30mph, airbags would inflate to minimise the impact. We knew there was a 60% chance of success.

At 3am on Christmas Day 2003 we were in the Open University office waiting to hear from the Beagle when it landed. It didn't call. So we waited for the next pass three hours later. It still didn't call. There was a whole long series of things that we, and the Beagle, had to do when it didn't get in contact, so we went through all of these things until February. And still nothing happened. Then we had to say that hope was lost. Thousands of kids that morning woke up and asked: 'What happened to Beagle 2?' Because Britain doesn't have a space programme, all of that enthusiasm has been lost. Britain is the world's fifth-richest nation, but the 17th in terms of space expenditure.

In the last month Nasa has asked me to research another Beagle for part of the attempt to put a manned base on the Moon by 2020. In the run-up to establishing a base, probes will be sent to find out what's there – a programme called Lunar Sortie. The idea is that people like us have our technology ready so if there is an opportunity then we are ready to go. It's nice to be recognised because it vindicates our mission. As usual, we haven't got any money yet and it'll be more difficult to get this time, but we'll damn well try. **COLIN PILLINGER**

Professor Colin Pillinger (pictured) is a planetary scientist at the Open University. He was the principal investigator and lead advocate for the ultimately unsuccessful Beagle 2 mission to Mars in 2003

The planets of our solar system

Mercury ***Distance from Sun*** *57,910,000km* ***Diameter*** *4,880km* ***Rotational period (1 Earth day)*** *59 days* ***Orbital period (1 Earth year)*** *88 days* ***Average temperature*** *-200C to +500C* ***Atmosphere*** *42% helium; 42% sodium; 15% oxygen; 1% other* ***Moons*** *0*

Named after the speedy Roman winged messenger, Mercury was first mentioned by the Babylonians in 3,000BC and finally explored by the Mariner 10 spacecraft in 1974. The planet is pockmarked with craters caused by asteroids and meteors regularly smashing into its surface. Despite Mercury's proximity to the Sun, it is believed that ice could exist under the surface.

Venus ***Distance from Sun*** *108,200,000km* ***Diameter*** *12,104km* ***Rotational period*** *243 days* ***Orbital period*** *224.7 days* ***Average temperature*** *450C* ***Atmosphere*** *96% carbon dioxide; 4% nitrogen (+ trace amounts of other gases)* ***Moons*** *0*

Referred to as Earth's sister planet, as it is similar in size, mass, density and volume, Venus is one of only two planets in the solar system that rotate from east to west (the other is Uranus). A heavy carbon-dioxide atmosphere and clouds composed of sulphuric acid surround the planet, and volcanos rule the landscape with lava flows hundreds of miles long. Venus was named after the goddess of love and beauty because it is one of the brightest and most beautiful planets in the solar system.

Earth ***Distance from Sun*** *149,600,000km* ***Diameter*** *12,756km* ***Rotational period*** *1 day* ***Orbital period*** *365.256 days* ***Average temperature*** *7C* ***Atmosphere*** *77% nitrogen; 21% oxygen; 2% other* ***Moons*** *1*

Earth (whose name can be traced through Germanic roots back to the Latin *terra*, meaning ground) has a powerful and extensive magnetic field, distorted by solar winds into a teardrop shape, which shields the surface from nearly all the Sun's harmful radiation, allowing life forms to exist. A three-mile wide 'second moon' called Cruithne passes us every 385 years – its irregular orbit means it has not yet achieved official moon status; however, it is expected that within 3,000 years this orbit will become more regular.

Mars ***Distance from Sun*** *227,940,000km* ***Diameter*** *6,794km* ***Rotational period*** *25 hours* ***Orbital period*** *687 days* ***Average temperature*** *-200C to +20C* ***Atmosphere*** *95% carbon dioxide; 2.7% nitrogen; 1.6% argon; 0.7% other* ***Moons*** *2*

Believed throughout history to be the planet most likely to harbour alien life, Mars has lines crossing its surface which ancient and modern astronomers interpreted as signs of complex irrigation systems. In 1965, Mariner 4 dispelled these theories by proving that the surface is bare, and we now know that the self-sterilising soil cannot sustain life. However, the possible presence of water and chemical activity in the soil indicates that organisms could have lived there in the distant past.

Jupiter ***Distance from Sun*** *778,330,000km* ***Diameter*** *142,984km* ***Rotational period*** *9.9 hours* ***Orbital period*** *4,333 days* ***Average temperature*** *-150C* ***Atmosphere*** *90% hydrogen; 10% helium* ***Moons*** *at least 63*

Jupiter ('king of the solar system') is the largest planet – more than 1,000 Earths could fit inside it – and is made almost entirely of gas: at its core the pressure is so great that hydrogen atoms are broken up, creating a point at which hydrogen becomes metallic. Jupiter's Great Red Spot is a massive storm twice the size of Earth, and its 250mph winds have been swirling for at least 300 years.

Saturn ***Distance from Sun*** *1,429,400,000km* ***Diameter*** *120,536km* ***Rotational period*** *10 hours* ***Orbital period*** *10,759 days* ***Average temperature*** *-180C* ***Atmosphere*** *97% hydrogen; 3% helium* ***Moons*** *at least 56*

Investigated by the Voyager expeditions in 1980-81, Saturn is flattened at the poles due to its incredibly fast rotation. It is the only planet less dense than water – it would float in a large-enough ocean. Its rings contain a significant amount of water, as millions of tiny icebergs, some only a few centimetres big, orbit the planet. Named after the god of agriculture and harvest and father of Jupiter, who overthrew him as king of the gods, Saturn is in the same family of gas giants as Jupiter, yet despite its massive size is still usurped by Jupiter.

Uranus ***Distance from Sun*** *2,870,990,000km* ***Diameter*** *51,118km* ***Rotational period*** *17.9 hours* ***Orbital period*** *84 years* ***Average temperature*** *-200C* ***Atmosphere*** *83% hydrogen; 15% helium; methane 2%* ***Moons*** *27*

Named after the Greek god of the sky due to its light blue colour, Uranus was discovered by William Herschel in 1787. It is tipped on its side, perhaps because of a collision with a planet-sized body billions of years ago – and in 1989, Voyager 2 discovered that this has resulted in the magnetic field developing a tail shaped like a long corkscrew behind the planet.

Neptune ***Distance from Sun*** *4,504,300,000km* ***Diameter*** *49,492km* ***Rotational period*** *19 hours* ***Orbital period*** *165 years* ***Average temperature*** *-220C* ***Atmosphere*** *85% hydrogen; 13% helium; 2% methane* ***Moons*** *13*

The last of the gas giants (the others are Jupiter, Saturn and Uranus), Neptune boasts the strongest winds found on any planet – they can attain up to 1,200mph near the Great Dark Spot (similar to Jupiter's Great Red Spot, and the size of Earth).

The 10 best-named celestial bodies

Several thousand asteroids clutter our solar system. They are named by their discoverer, subject to approval by the International Astronomical Union's Committee for Small Body Nomenclature. Here are 10 of the more imaginative...

1 **Hergé** Discovered in 1953
The creator of Tintin is the only comic-book artist in space.

2 **Lancelot** Discovered in 1960
Joins planets Arthur and Guinevere in a cosmic love triangle.

3 **Swissair** Discovered in 1968
The national airline acquires a new route.

4 **Karl Marx** Discovered in 1969
The same Russian astronomer who claimed a planet for the economist also named asteroids after US author Jack London and martyred Chilean musician Victor Jara.

5 **Carlsberg** Discovered in 1979
The brewery founder Jacob Jacobsen funded a Danish scientific foundation. Hence, hic, this tribute.

6 **Zappafrank** Discovered in 1980
For Czechs, and astronomers, the rock star was a symbol of liberty in the Cold War years.

7 **Purple Mountain** Discovered in 1980
Not a Grateful Dead track but a major Chinese observatory.

8 **Nostalgia** Discovered in 1980
Planet names ain't what they used to be...

9 **Chaucer** Discovered in 1981
Many creative luminaries are also planets – Kandinsky, Chopin, Shakespeare, Fellini, Pushkin, Handel, Duke Ellington – but only Geoffrey Chaucer is also a lunar crater.

10 **Tardis** Discovered in 1984
Dr Who's craft (acronym for Time and Relative Dimensions in Space) is officially out there.

What is...

A star

Stars are formed when clouds of dust and hydrogen coalesce. As the cloud gets smaller and smaller, pulled together by its gravitational field, friction causes its molecules to heat up until it reaches a critical temperature, around 1 million degrees Kelvin. Hydrogen starts to burn into helium through the process of nuclear fusion, eventually releasing energy equivalent to a billion hydrogen bombs going off every second, radiating light and heat into space. Thus a star is born.

A star's colour is determined by its temperature – the hottest are blue, the coolest red. In a medium-hot star like our own Sun, hydrogen burns and helium forms at its core. After billions of years, the star's hydrogen is used up, its core contracts and the star begins to burn its helium, turning it into carbon and oxygen. In smaller stars, like our Sun, this process comes to a dead end. The star expands to become a Red Giant blowing off an outer shell of material. The remaining core is known as a White Dwarf, which slowly cools, growing dimmer and dimmer until it stops shining.

Massive stars – those with masses more than two times that of the Sun – end in a more dramatic fashion. They burn up their carbon and oxygen, through nuclear fusion, to make heavier and heavier elements until they suffer a catastrophic collapse as the fuel runs out and the star's gravity pulls material inward. The result is a supernova explosion that blasts material and radiation out into space and leaves behind a tiny, super-dense neutron star or, in some cases, a black hole. **Robin McKie**

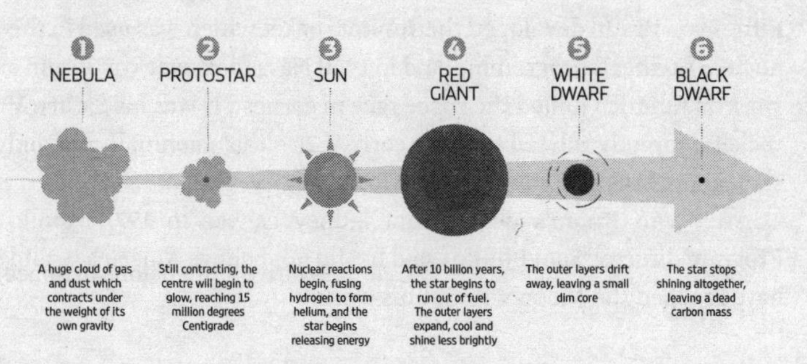

Wernher von Braun

(b. 23 March 1912; d. 16 June 1977)
Rocket scientist

Wernher Magnus Maximilian Freiherr von Braun was hooked on astronomy, outer space and rockets from an early age. As a 12-year-old he scared a crowd in Berlin by setting off fireworks attached to a toy wagon in the street, and following his schooling he joined the Spaceflight Society at the Technical University of Berlin, where he began work on liquid-fuelled rocket flight.

Dr von Braun's work was soon co-opted by the army, and under the National Socialist government he developed the trail-blazing V-2 rockets which could reach heights of 50 miles. When the first V-2 rocket was launched at London in September 1944 von Braun commented: 'The rocket worked perfectly except for landing on the wrong planet.' The rockets dropped on their targets at four times the speed of sound. An estimated 7,000 died from the V-2 raids while 20,000 people died in the concentration camps where they worked to produce them.

> *We can lick gravity, but sometimes the paperwork is overwhelming.*
>
> Wernher von Braun

After the war von Braun was taken to America in the secretive Operation Paperclip which rounded up German scientists for US programmes. In the Fifties von Braun developed the Jupiter rocket which was used in the nuclear warhead programme, and in 1960 Nasa took over von Braun's work as America joined the space race in earnest. It was his Saturn V rocket – directly related to those early V-2s – that eventually carried six teams of US astronauts to the Moon.

After von Braun's death from kidney cancer in 1977, Apollo Program director Sam Phillips said he did not believe America would have reached the Moon without his work.

Top 10 films about space

***Destination Moon* (1950, Irving Pichel)** The first major sci-fi film made in the US, it shows a nuclear-powered rocket flying to the Moon. The film won an Academy Award for best special effects.

***2001: A Space Odyssey* (1968, Stanley Kubrick)** A team of astronauts sets out to uncover a mysterious monolith embedded in the Moon.

***Solaris* (1972, Andrei Tarkovsky)** This adaptation of the Stanislaw Lem novel deals with a crew on the planet Solaris confronted by figures from their painful repressed memories.

***Star Wars* (1977, George Lucas)** In a galaxy far, far away, a psychopathic emperor and his servant are threatening annihilation. It is up to farm-boy Luke Skywalker to rescue captured Princess Leia and save the universe.

***Alien* (1979, Ridley Scott)** Nostromo, a mining spaceship en route to Earth, takes a detour to another planet after receiving a distress signal. The crew discovers a hive colony of aliens and realise that the signal was actually a warning.

***Flash Gordon* (1980, Mike Hodges)** Flash Gordon is a football hero charged with saving the world from Ming the Merciless.

***Star Trek: The Wrath of Khan* (1982, Nicholas Meyer)** Captain Kirk and the Enterprise crew face their old foe, the superhuman Khan, who has returned from exile to wreak havoc on the universe.

***ET: The Extra-Terrestrial* (1982, Steven Spielberg)** A 10-year-old boy befriends an alien who is trying to make his way home after being stranded on Earth.

***Armageddon* (1998, Michael Bay)** Nasa discovers a doomsday asteroid the size of Texas on a collision course with Earth and sends its finest team to investigate.

***Sunshine* (2007, Danny Boyle)** A team of scientists is sent on a last-ditch mission to deliver a huge nuclear bomb to the Sun in the hope that it will reignite the dying star.

Calling ET

SETI hieroglyphs and the Arecibo broadcast of 1974

In 1961, scientist and SETI (Search for Extraterrestrial Intelligence) pioneer Frank Drake predicted that of our galaxy's 100 billion solar systems, anywhere between 30bn and 77bn of them are likely to host some form of life that we could realistically communicate with. As a result of his findings, in 1974 Drake's SETI team broadcast a message from the massive Arecibo satellite dish in Puerto Rico directed towards the star cluster M13, roughly 21,000 light years away. Designed to give any potential recipients information about our biochemical make-up and whereabouts, the message was built from 1,679 zeros and ones in the hope that an intelligent race could recognise that this number was the product of two prime numbers – 73 and 23. Arrange these zeros and ones into 73 rows of 23 characters, and the picture shown below would reveal itself.

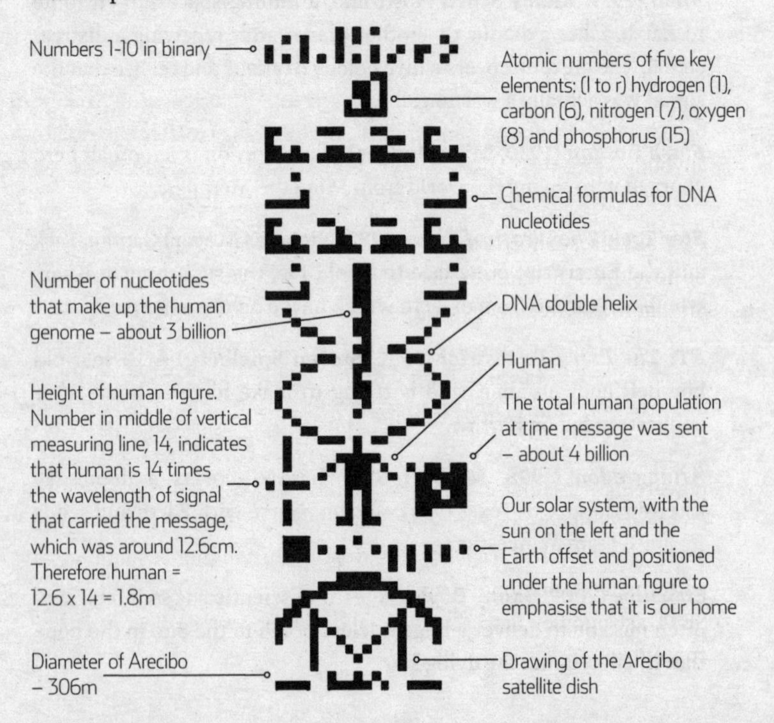

Four other attempts to contact aliens

Since Drake's Seventies experiments, the SETI programme's raison d'être has been to track the galaxy for distinctive radio signals that might indicate extraterrestrial life. In August 1977 they thought the search had paid off when a SETI professor heard what is now known as the Wow! signal – a sound so strong and so similar to that expected that its discoverer wrote 'Wow!' on the printout. The signal was never heard again, even by much stronger radio telescopes, and was written off as an anomaly. Here are four other attempts to communicate with alien life...

1 Burning symbols In 1820, German mathematician Karl Friedrich Gauss proposed cutting a giant right-angle triangle into the Siberian pine forests, giving Pythagoras a universal audience. Austrian Joseph von Littrow expanded on the idea 20 years later when he suggested that giant triangles, circles and squares be dug into the Sahara, filled with kerosene and set ablaze. Neither idea ever got off the ground.

2 Morse code A variation of Morse code was posited throughout the early 20th century as a way of easily sending a message through space. It would use a prime-number system – presaging the Arecibo broadcast – or squared numbers (16, 25, 36, 49 etc) to demonstrate to anybody listening that intelligent beings were sending premeditated signals. Then the senders would just wait for a reply.

3 Gold discs Before Frank Drake completed the Arecibo broadcast, he developed the Pioneer plaque in 1972 with astronomer Carl Sagan. Similar to the Arecibo message in style, it was etched onto the Pioneer spacecraft in the hope that a wandering extraterrestrial might stumble across it. Drake and Sagan also sent a gold-plated record full of music and photos along with the Voyager probes in 1977.

4 Lasers One idea being developed for the future is the use of high-powered lasers, and Drake has already put forward his desire to create a holographic movie about life on Earth, while other researchers are still transfixed by the idea of sending out numerical patterns. Probably one of the most inventive ideas has come from SETI astronomer Seth Shostak, who wants to send up the entire contents of Google.

The insider: space memorabilia collector

Leslie Cantwell

I am *not* an autograph hunter; I don't do autographs. Nor am I a space nerd. When Neil and Buzz were about to land on the Moon I was a young man in bed, drunk, and my flatmate woke me to watch it on TV. But later I got hooked on the Apollo programme. You've got to actually stand under a Saturn V rocket and look up to understand the audacity of what they did. It's like sending St Paul's Cathedral into space. Kennedy said: 'Let's get Americans on the Moon', and for the next 10 years 30,000 people worked on it. What fascinates me is the objectivity, pace and team spirit.

It started in 1981. I was at the Hanover Book Festival when this diminutive fellow grabbed my arm. I thought: 'Oh no, another God squad guy', but it was Jim Irwin from Apollo 15 and he gave me a photo of himself on the Moon and wrote 'With love from the Moon' on it. He impressed me as such a gentle soul.

> *It's different, but it's very pretty out here. I suppose they are going to make a big deal of all this.*
>
> Neil Armstrong speaking from the Moon

About eight years ago I got into Dante and especially *Paradiso*: 'I have been to that heaven where His light beams brightest and seen things that none, returning, has the knowledge or the power to repeat.' And then: 'O Great Apollo! Grant the strenuous wing this ultimate labour needs.' And it made me think of Jim and the other astronauts and how they had seen this amazing thing that this incredible poet had imagined 700 years ago.

I went to the Nasa archives and dug around and looked at the photographs – they struck me as mind-boggling, like works of art. So I began collecting these prints and getting them blown up and autographed by the astronauts. I've got Gene Kranz's (the Nasa flight controller who guided Apollo 13 back to Earth) paperweight and a centimetre square of gold mylar coating from Apollo 11. It's all quite expensive: Sotheby's auctions Nasa prints for $1,000 (£500); a page from the Apollo 11 lunar landing chart costs $180,000

(£90,000). Most importantly, I've got the world's largest collection of space prints.

I've met all 12 men who have walked on the Moon now and many of the others involved. There was a massive hierarchy on the programme and the price of an autograph reflects that: Armstrong then Aldrin, Young, Collins, Scott, Cernan etc. Most were ex-test pilots, fighter jocks. Armstrong – he of the Mona Lisa smile – is shy, very quiet, and won't sign many autographs, which means a signed picture is worth $10,000 (£5,000) – I've got two.

The most complicated astronaut is Buzz. He was supposed to be the first on the Moon but they jumped Neil above him when they realised what a big deal it would be. Many of the astronauts sign their names 'Sixth guy on the Moon' or 'Last guy on the Moon'. But Buzz doesn't write 'Second guy on the Moon'. He is like a film star: he'll wear his Légion d'Honneur medal to a dinner dance, he has his own publicity department, he's had plastic surgery and he charges a fortune for a signature – £100 a go.

I've started trying to get the astronauts to write in their own hands snatches of poetry onto my prints. They tend to be jocks, quite anti-poetry and it's a lot easier to get them to write patriotic slogans, but with persuasion – and bucks – I've managed it. To get a fighter-jock moonwalker to write a canto from Dante's *Divine Comedy* bridges a gap of 700 years. Dante was writing an allegory about the heavens, and these guys have seen it. It's esoteric, an art thing, and a lot of people don't get it. But I think the words written by the astronauts personalise the images and bring them alive. **Leslie Cantwell**

Leslie Cantwell began collecting images from the Apollo missions eight years ago and is probably the UK's leading space collector. He now spends much of his time forging relationships with the moonwalkers

Five ways to buy a little space

1 Take a trip to space £107,000
Richard Branson's Virgin Galactic is expected to be up and running by late 2008, which will give you around 2.5 hours of weightlessness more than 100km above the Earth. If you can't wait that long, the Russians will happily fly you up to the International Space Station for a paltry $30 million (£14.8m).

2 Invest in some lunar real estate £19.99/acre
Moon Estates – the only company licensed in the UK to sell property on the Moon – will happily send you a certificate. Dennis Hope (aka the Head Cheese), an American who claimed every planet and moon in the solar system in 1980, swears it's all bona fide. Its website does admit, however: 'What the future brings, we do not know... In short, there are no guarantees (except our 30-day money-back guarantee, of course).'

3 Buy a slice of meteorite £100-£4,000
If you've ever felt the burning desire to own some 'exceptionally fresh Martian basaltic shergottite' or maybe even some 'Olivine gabbro' then www.catchafallingstar.com can satisfy your needs. They will even turn your purchase into some fetching jewellery.

4 Have yourself a space funeral £2,500
There's nothing quite like saying goodbye to a loved one by blasting their ashes as far into space as humanly possible. The first funeral took place in April 1997 when the ashes of 23 people, including those of *Star Trek* creator Gene Roddenberry, were sent into space aboard the Pegasus rocket. *Star Trek* writer/producer John Lucas and James Doohan (Scotty in *Star Trek*) have subsequently had their ashes beamed up aboard a Celestis Memorial Spaceflight.

5 Name a star £25-£69
For £69, www.starlistings.co.uk will type your star's name ('in a constellation of your choice') into their computer, although the star's new name won't actually be recognised anywhere other than on the company's database, as the International Astronomical Union is the only group that can officially name celestial bodies.

Lost in space

The demotion of Pluto

When is a planet not a planet? When 424 astronomers say so. That was how many members of the International Astronomical Union (IAU) took the historic vote in August 2006 that saw Pluto (pictured) downgraded to the status of 'dwarf' planet, alongside the recently discovered UB313 (Eris) and former asteroid Ceres.

For a piece of cosmic regime change, the ruling was a suitably murky affair that saw the findings of the IAU's committee on planetary status summarily dumped, while the vote to reclassify Pluto came only on the last day of the conference, after most delegates had gone home. Many astronomers were left in dismay. Remarked Alan Stern, leader of Nasa's New Horizons mission to Pluto: 'Less than 5% of the world's astronomers voted. I'm embarrassed for astronomy.'

Also found wanting was the IAU's new definition of a real planet, which must have 'cleared the neighbourhood around its orbit', meaning that there are no neighbouring asteroids and flotsam – a condition clearly flouted by Jupiter, which has some 50,000 Trojan asteroids. 'This definition stinks,' came Stern's judgment. 'Confusing and unfortunate,' agreed Owen Gingerich, astronomer emeritus at Harvard.

Can Pluto, backed by popular sentiment, make a comeback? Watch this space. NEIL SPENCER

Pluto factfile The Roman god of the underworld was as spooky as his predecessor, the Greek Hades. He was also a wealth god (his subjects could only increase). Plutocrat and plutonic have become common descriptions like saturnine, but for many Pluto's meaning is forever linked to Mickey Mouse's goofy hound, named after Pluto's discovery in 1930.

The Observer archive: historic moments in space exploration

The first men on the Moon

(21 July 1969)

While our minds last Tuesday still burned with those spectral images of men cavorting like children of the gods on their lunar playground, a drawing started circulating here. It was a sketch of Wernher von Braun's idea for a manned Mars ship.

Most of us had seen it before, but now we looked at it with special interest, even the cynics. For now we knew that Americans can – and will – go where they choose in space. It wasn't the worldwide excitement that made the change. It certainly wasn't all that moonshine about 'man fulfilling his destiny'. It wasn't even that Apollo 11, like its predecessors, had performed so flawlessly.

For me, at least, it was the quiet, obsessive concentration on every single detail of the men in charge of the flight. They didn't raise the Stars and Stripes here until the last astronaut touched the deck of the recovery ship. By that time most of the press had gone home. The men in charge would not relax until each tiny step of the mission had been safely taken. Their responsibility and maturity were deeply impressive. And so, when the talk did turn to at the week's end towards ranging over the face of the moon, sending men out to the planets, and taming the near-earth reaches of space, one knew they would do it.

And suddenly one wants them to, despite everything. Even the cost seems unimportant. The old arguments about going to the moon or cleaning up the mess down here seem irrelevant. A nation that has the audacity to do what it has just done, and which spends $5,000 million a year on TV sets, $3,000 million on pleasure boats and $1,100 million on ski equipment (the last two items more than covering the total annual space budget), can find the surplus wealth to do almost anything. And go to Mars. But first it must want to do so.

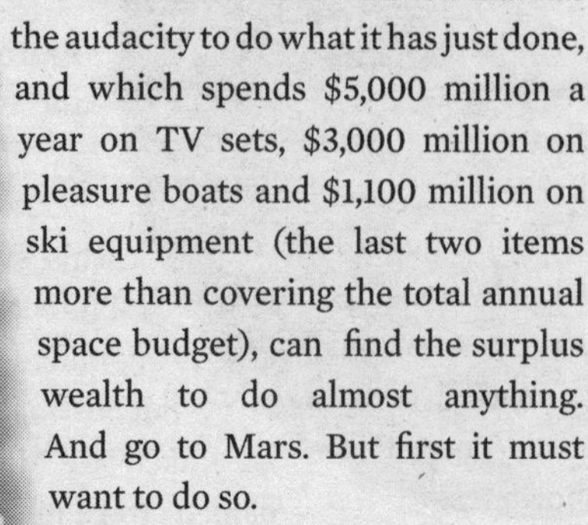

THE OBSERVER REVIEW

...sch reports from Houston: 'A nation that has the audacity to do what it has just done, and ...ends 5,000 million dollars a year on TV sets, 3,000 million on pleasure boats and 1,100 million ...on ski equipment, can find the surplus wealth to do almost anything. And go to Mars.'

Deep down, most Americans don't care about poverty or urban blight. But these men do care fiercely about space. They fought for it with an apathetic or downright distrustful Congress and public. They overcame staggering technical and organisational difficulties, and they finally triumphed. It is in this sense – a sharp reminder that it is not money but men who get things done – that we have seen mankind enlarged.

Gerald Leach, 27 July 1969

Factfile: At 0256 GMT on 21 July 1969, Neil Armstrong stepped out of the moonlander and into the history books. As well as raising the Stars and Stripes, Armstrong and his companion Buzz Aldrin unveiled a plaque signed by President Nixon which read: 'Here men from the planet Earth first set foot upon the Moon July 1969 AD. We came in peace for all mankind'

One small step: the story of that famous line

Neil Armstrong's sentence ('That's one small step for man, one giant leap for mankind'), spoken 250,000 miles above our heads in July 1969, managed in only 11 words to sum up the massive technological milestone human science had just passed. But could it be that his line, heard by more than a billion people, was fluffed? Rumours have circulated ever since that what Armstrong (who came up with the poignant words himself, gazing out of the window in the six-hour gap between landing on the Moon and stepping out of the Lunar Module) had intended to say was: 'That's one small step for a man, one giant leap for mankind', and that the 'a' was dropped in all the lunar excitement. In fact, without it, the sentence doesn't really make sense – grammatically it means: 'That's one small step for mankind, one giant leap for mankind.'

It took the painstaking work of Australian computer programmer Peter Shann Ford to finally vindicate Armstrong's claim that he delivered the line perfectly. Using hi-tech computer equipment to analyse the recording, in 2006 Ford discovered an 'a', previously masked by transmission interference, lasting a total of 35 milliseconds – 10 times too quick to be heard. Is this all just a little slice of grammatical pedantry? Armstrong's authorised biographer James Hansen doesn't think so: 'It was meant for all mankind, and it's important to have it correct.'

Yuri Gagarin

(b. 9 March 1934; d. 27 March 1968)
Cosmonaut

On 12 April 1961, Yuri Alekseyevich Gagarin was blasted into the history books atop a Vostok rocket to become the first human in space. The trip lasted 108 minutes and Gagarin orbited Earth once, recalling: 'I saw for the first time how beautiful our planet is. Mankind, let us preserve and increase this beauty, and not destroy it!'

Gagarin had been born into poverty, the son of manual labourers on a collective farm in Smolensk, northwest Russia. In 1942, the area was occupied by invading Germans, and his youngest brother was hanged while his sisters were taken away to labour camps. During an apprenticeship with an ironworks, Gagarin was chosen to go to a technical school in Moscow, where he joined the local Aero Club and learned to fly light aircraft. He was then chosen for military flight training, excelling in the harsh conditions of the Arctic Circle.

> *“I could have gone on flying through space forever.*
> Yuri Gagarin

In 1960 he was one of 20 pilots selected for the cosmonaut programme. Due to his excellent physical and mental aptitude and diminutive height (he was just 5ft 2in) Gagarin was given, at the last minute, the assignment of being the first human to orbit Earth: 'What beauty. I saw clouds and their light shadows on the distant dear Earth... It is surrounded by a light blue aureole that gradually darkens, becoming turquoise, dark blue, violet and finally coal black.'

Gagarin's flight made him an instant worldwide celebrity and he became a deputy director at Star City, training cosmonauts for space flight, but he also decided to retrain as a fighter pilot. During a routine training flight in 1968 his MiG-15 crashed, and he and his instructor were killed. Gagarin is buried in the walls of the Kremlin in Red Square.

Ten classic novels about space

***From the Earth to the Moon* (1865) by Jules Verne** Members of the Baltimore Gun Club launch a rocket to the Moon, and the stakes are raised when someone volunteers to go along with it.

***The War of the Worlds* (1898) by HG Wells** Martians invade Earth and destroy much of London and the surrounding countryside before they succumb to a deadly disease.

***The Martian Chronicles* (1950) by Ray Bradbury** Twenty years after the Great War and on the brink of human civilisation's collapse, a group escapes to Mars.

***The Foundation Trilogy* (1951-53) by Isaac Asimov** Psychohistorian Hari Seldon predicts a new dark age will sweep mankind and sets about recording all human knowledge in the *Encyclopedia Galactica* in Asimov's towering sci-fi series.

***Martian Time-Slip* (1964) by Philip K Dick** Humans have colonised an arid Mars and the only thing worth more than water is 10-year-old Jack Bohlen, who it is believed can see into the future.

***The Moon is a Harsh Mistress* (1966) by Robert A Heinlein** It is 2076 and the lunar colonies are revolting against Earth's authority. A band of dissidents, including a one-armed computer jock, take up the fight.

***Downward to the Earth* (1970) by Robert Silverberg** Gundersen, an ex-colonial supervisor, makes a pilgrimage to an old colonised planet, seeking atonement from those he once exploited.

***The Hitchhiker's Guide to the Galaxy* (1979) by Douglas Adams** Before Earth is obliterated Arthur Dent is whisked away on an intergalactic journey to ascertain the meaning of life, the universe and everything.

***Contact* (1985) by Carl Sagan** A team of scientists travels into space after receiving what they believe to be a message from extraterrestrials.

***Songs of Distant Earth* (1986) by Arthur C Clarke** Thalassa has long been a utopian planet until the Magellan ship arrives with 1 million refugees from the last mad days of Earth.

The stargazer's diary

This calendar shows what will be appearing in the sky over the coming year. All should be visible to the naked eye (the planets will look like stars – Jupiter in opposition will seem to be the brightest star in the sky). One degree is equal to two Moon diameters, so on 7 January, if you look about 8 Moon diameters north of the Moon itself, you will see Jupiter as a bright star.

November 07

17 Leonid meteor shower at its peak at 7.30am
22 Monocerotids meteor shower at its peak
9 ○ New Moon (best for stargazing)
24 ● Full Moon (worst for stargazing)

December 07

13 Geminids meteor shower at its peak at 8.45pm
22 WINTER SOLSTICE The point at which the Earth's axis is tilted the most away from the Sun – it signifies the height of winter and the longest night of the year. The Ursids meteor shower is also at its peak
24 Mars is in opposition at 12pm
9 ○ **24** ●

January 08

2 PERIHELION The point at which the Earth is closest to the Sun (147 million km away)
5 Venus is 7N of the Moon at 3am
7 Jupiter is 4N of the Moon at 10am
9 Mercury is 0.3N of the Moon at 4pm
20 Mars is 1S of the Moon at 12am
22 Mercury is at its greatest Eastern elongation from the Sun at 5am
25 Saturn is 3N of the Moon at 4am
8 ○ **22** ●

February 08

4 Jupiter is 4N of the Moon at 6am; Venus is 4N of the Moon at 12pm
6 Mercury is at its Inferior conjunction at 6pm
7 Mercury is 5N of the Moon at 2am
16 Mars is 2S of the Moon at 8am
21 LUNAR ECLIPSE at 3am; Saturn is 3N of the Moon at 10am
24 Saturn is in opposition to the Sun at 10am
7 ○ **21** ●

March 08

3 Jupiter is 4N of the Moon 2am; Mercury is at its greatest Western elongation at 11am
5 Mercury is 0.2N of the Moon at 2pm; Venus is 0.2S of the Moon at 7pm
15 Mars is 2S of the Moon at 3am
19 Saturn is 2N of the Moon at 2pm
20 SPRING EQUINOX The point at which the Sun is positioned directly over the Earth's equator, and so is shining equally on the northern and southern hemispheres at 5.48pm
30 Jupiter is 3N of the Moon at 6pm
7 ○ **21** ●

April 07

4 Venus is 4S of the Moon at 10pm
5 Mercury is 5S of the Moon at 8am
12 Mars is 1S of the Moon at 6am
15 Saturn is 2N of the Moon at 5pm
16 Mercury is at its Superior conjunction at 7am
27 Jupiter is 3N of the Moon at 6am
6 ○ **20** ●

May 08

4 Venus is 6S of the Moon at 8pm
6 Mercury is 2S of the Moon at 10pm
10 Mars is 0.2S of the Moon at 2pm
12 Saturn is 3N of the Moon at 10pm
14 Mercury is at its greatest eastern elongation at 4am
24 Jupiter is 2N of the Moon at 12pm
5 ❍ **20** ●

June 08

3 Venus is 5S of the Moon at 5pm
4 Mercury is 6S of the Moon at 4am
7 Mercury is at its Inferior conjunction at 3pm
8 Mars is 1N of the Moon at 2am
9 Venus is at its Superior conjunction at 4am; Saturn is 3N of the Moon at 7am
20 Pluto is in opposition at 8pm; SUMMER SOLSTICE The point at which the Earth's axis is tilted the most towards the Sun – it signifies the height of summer and the shortest day of the year at 11.59pm
3 ❍ **18** ●

July 08

1 Mercury is 8S of the Moon at 2pm; Mercury is at its greatest western elongation at 6pm
3 Venus is 2S of the Moon at 2pm
4 APHELION The point at which the Earth is furthest away from the Sun (152 million km away)
6 Mars is 2N of the Moon at 4pm; Saturn is 3N of the Moon at 8pm
9 Jupiter is in opposition at 8am
17 Jupiter is 3N of the Moon at 1pm
29 Mercury is at its Superior conjunction 8pm
3 ❍ **18** ●

August 08

1 SOLAR ECLIPSE A total eclipse will be visible from Canada, central Russia, Mongolia and China. In the UK we will be able to see a partial eclipse from around 8.30am until 10am.
1 Mercury is 1N of the Moon at 4pm
2 Capricornids meteor shower at its peak; Venus is 2N of the Moon at 1pm
3 Saturn is 3N of the Moon at 11am
4 Mars is 4N of the Moon at 9am
12 Perseids meteor shower (possibly the most spectacular of all meteor showers)
13 Jupiter is 3N of the Moon at 3pm
15 Neptune is in opposition at 8am
16 Partial Lunar Eclipse: 7.30pm-10.45pm
31 Saturn is 4N of the Moon at 2am
1 ❍ **16** ●

September 08

1 Venus is 5N of the Moon at 4pm; Mercury is 3N of the Moon at 9pm
2 Mars is 5N of the Moon at 4am
11 Mercury is at its greatest eastern elongation at 4am
13 Uranus is in opposition at 2am
22 AUTUMN EQUINOX at 3.44pm
27 Saturn is 4N of the Moon at 4pm
30 Mercury is 1N of the Moon at 10am
29 ❍ **15** ●

October 07

1 Mars is 5N of the Moon at 12am; Venus is 5N of the Moon at 11pm
6 Mercury is at its Inferior conjunction at 9pm
7 Jupiter is 2N of the Moon at 8am
21 Orionids meteor shower at its peak 6am
22 Mercury is at its greatest western elongation at 9am
25 Saturn is 4N of the Moon 4am
27 Mercury is 7N of the Moon 12pm
29 Mars is 5N of the Moon 10pm
28 ❍ **14** ●

Note: Greatest elongation means that one of the inferior planets (between Earth and the Sun, ie Mercury or Venus) is at its furthest point from the Sun from the Earth's point of view. At this point it will look like a quarter Moon. Inferior conjunction means it will pass between the Sun and Earth. Superior conjunction means it will again be in line with the Sun and Earth (looking like a full Moon). A superior planet (any planet further away from the Sun than Earth) in opposition to the Sun is at its closest to the Earth, and so at this point the planet is visible all night and shines at its maximum strength

All information taken from the 2008 British Astronomical Association Handbook. For further information or to become a member, visit www.britastro.org

The insider: moonwalker

Edgar Mitchell

Going to the Moon was not something I'd ever considered. I started flying at 13, had a pilot's license by 16, and was drafted on graduation in 1951 as a naval aviator in the Korean War. In October 1957 I came home to take up test-pilot duty. Sputnik had just been launched and I realised humans would be right behind robot spacecraft. It seemed like an interesting thing to go for, so I did. By the time I was selected in 1966, aged 36, I was the first astronaut to have both test-pilot credentials and a PhD from a major technical school, MIT (Massachusetts Institute of Technology).

I don't think we were frightened – we were test pilots, and most of us had been in war, in places where survival was difficult. We were chosen because we could handle that kind of thing. You had to come to terms with your fear of death and put it aside to perform your mission. Our flight commander would always say as the rockets fired up: 'OK, it's sweaty palms time' to lighten the tension, because that was when it could all go wrong.

> *"Man is an artifact designed for space travel. He is not designed to remain in his present biologic state any more than a tadpole is designed to remain a tadpole.*
> **William Burroughs**

Every mission to the Moon built upon the successes of the past, but each one also pushed harder, went further, had a more difficult task. The first mission (Apollo 11) was to prove we could land and return. The next (Apollo 12) was to prove we could land precisely where we wanted to. Our job with Apollo 14 was to go into the Fra Mauro Highlands, a more challenging, mountainous area covered with meteor impacts and dust. We had to do the first proper science and then do a 3km geology trek up to the 750ft-deep Cone Crater, collecting samples as we went. Physically, walking on the

Moon is like walking on a trampoline wearing four overcoats – you've got the pressure suit on, you're puffed up like the Michelin man. It weighs about 470lb on Earth, but only 70lb on the Moon. We brought back about 95lb of deep lunar material, and that told the geologists back home what was going on deep inside the Moon.

We also did a few experiments on the side: Alan Shepard took his golf shots, and being a creature of science I did one on ESP to see if the experiments on telepathy, which had been successful in laboratories, could be done from such a distance. Despite Alan's claim that the golf balls went miles and miles, they actually went 50ft into a crater. Then I picked up a used piece of equipment and used it as a javelin, outthrowing his golf ball by six inches. You could call that the first Lunar Olympics, and I took gold!

The experience I had coming back was similar to that of many lunar-module pilots. Our tasks were completed, and we were just systems engineers on a well-functioning spacecraft with no major problems. So we looked out of the window. The capsule was essentially a rotating bullet, and every two minutes a 360-degree panorama containing the Earth, the Moon, the Sun and all the heavens was available to us in the window. That was a wild, wild experience. I realised that the Sun and the stars out there were the creators of matter in our universe and that the molecules in my body and those of my colleagues were manufactured in these ancient stars – instead of an intellectual experience, it became an emotional one. It was an ecstasy that lasted about three days, and I didn't know what it meant. Humans have always asked: 'How did we get here?', 'Where are we going?', 'What is this really all about?' – and I thought that as the first generation of spacefarers we should re-ask those questions.

It was so personal, so overwhelming, that most of us who had these types of experiences were very quiet about it when we got back. For me, going to the Moon had been a transcendental experience, and I was never the same after it. **Edgar Mitchell**

Dr Edgar Mitchell (pictured) landed on the Moon on 5 February 1971 and was the sixth man to walk on the lunar surface. He left Nasa in 1972 and founded the Institute of Noetic Sciences to study the nature of consciousness in relation to cosmology. A documentary about the Apollo Moon landings, In the Shadow of the Moon, *is in cinemas now*

Apocalypse soon?

Four ways the world could end

1 The Sun dies

The only doom-laden scenario that will definitely occur. However, we've got about 5 billion years before this happens, so don't panic just yet.

2 We go out like the dinosaurs

Another distinct possibility is that an asteroid or comet will slam into Earth, wiping out most if not all of mankind in seconds. Asteroid strikes occur about once every 300 years with differing degrees of destruction. In 1908, an asteroid just 60 metres in diameter exploded above Tunguska in Siberia, wiping out 80 million trees over 2,150 sq km. If that happened over an inhabited area, the death toll would be millions – and that was a small hit, predicted to happen about once every 100 years. The asteroid that killed off the dinosaurs was more than 10km across, and there are craters in Australia and Norway that suggest similar-sized rocks have hit in the distant past.

3 Gliese 710

A small dim star hurtling towards our solar system at 50,400km/hr that will miss Earth by about 40,000AU (quite a long way) in about 1.4m years, but by smashing into the Oort cloud (the outer layer of the solar system) it will send the millions of huge asteroids lying there rushing through the solar system and possibly at Earth (see above for what that could mean). And Gliese 710 is not alone: Barnard's star is expected to come remarkably close in just 10,000 years.

4 Hypernova

A massive dying star at least 40 times the size of our Sun collapsing into a black hole within 3,000 light years of Earth would be enough to kill off all life instantly, including bacteria, by bombarding the planet with extremely strong radiation, up to 1m times the strength of an X-ray. For now we're safe: the nearest massive star is some 7,500 light years away, still enough to do a little damage to our atmosphere and fry any satellites in the southern hemisphere, but not enough to penetrate down to the surface. Our solar system has already survived a few hypernovae, and now no more threatening stars remain.

What is...

A Milky Way

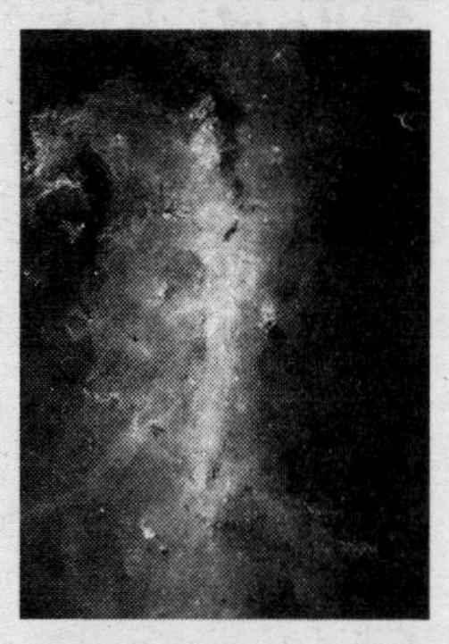

The Milky Way (pictured) is the galaxy in which our solar system is located. A galaxy is made up of billions or trillions of stars bound together by their own gravity, and there are millions of galaxies in the universe. All of the stars we see in our night sky belong to our own Milky Way, which is twisted into a spiral with four 'arms' extending from a main disk. The galaxy is estimated to contain at least 200 billion stars in the main disk, which is about 80,000 to 100,000 light years in diameter and about 250,000 to 300,000 light years in circumference. On a dark night, the Milky Way appears as a faint pale ribbon stretching across the sky. **Robin McKie**

G-force: how it feels to accelerate into space

Rather than being caused by gravity, g-force (or gravity force) expresses what it *feels* like to accelerate (or decelerate) in relation to gravity. In everyday life the force of gravity acting upon us means we are always experiencing 1*g*, however the rapid movement of coughing causes a g-force of 3.5*g* (meaning that for a split second you feel about 3.5 times heavier than normal). Even turning a corner while walking creates a small g-force, we're just so used to it that it doesn't feel unusual. Astronauts in space experience 0*g* (or weightlessness), while pilots or Formula 1 drivers regularly experience forces of 5-10*g*. It's thought that 15*g* is potentially deadly to humans, if sustained for more than a minute.

4.5*g* Oblivion rollercoaster, Alton Towers

50*g* Instruments on spacecraft have to be able to sustain gs of this magnitude

180*g* Survived by British F1 driver David Purley in 1977 when his car hit a wall at 173km/hr

A dog's life

Laika: the first living creature in orbit

Laika, a homeless three-year-old husky mongrel (pictured), was picked off a Moscow street by the Soviet authorities to be trained for the ultimate suicide mission: a one-way flight into space.

Soviet leader Nikita Khrushchev, who originally saw Sputnik as something of a novelty project undeserving of investment or time, suddenly decided space was where the Russians belonged after Sputnik 1's success in 1957 was splashed across the front pages of the world's media. To capitalise on this propaganda coup, he told his scientists to launch another Sputnik just a month later to commemorate the anniversary of the Bolshevik Revolution.

> *"We in Russia love dogs, too, but the dog in space is a real hero.*
> Moscow Radio

They quickly began training poor Laika (whose original name, Kudryavka, meaning Little Curly, was changed to Laika, or Barker, as it was thought western journalists could pronounce it more easily) by keeping her in progressively smaller cages. The spaceship itself was rushed and Laika's living quarters were about the size of a washing machine, with enough food and air to last just 10 days (Sputnik 2 was designed to be up there for six weeks).

On 3 November 1957, she was blasted into space and within an hour became the first animal to reach Earth's orbit. Not that she was enjoying it. Laika's heart rate quickly raced to three times her normal level, and the temperature in her cramped cabin increased to around 400C due to a computer malfunction.

Laika was dead after just five hours but the craft continued to orbit the Earth for six months before burning up on re-entry. She was lauded as a hero back in Russia and her image was printed on stamps and cigarette packets. The National Canine Defence League in Britain, however, was less pleased, keeping a minute's silence for every day she was in space. An American canine psychologist attempted to calm their fears though, declaring: 'This dog is happy to be part of something important.'

Ten unwitting astronauts

It is often animals who have the honour of boldly going where no man has gone before. Here are just 10 of the stranger creatures to have been blasted into space...

Fruit flies (USA, 1946) The first animals in space were sent up with corn seeds in a V-2 rocket.

Albert II the monkey (USA, 1949) A rhesus monkey and the first primate in space, again in a V-2. Don't ask what happened to Albert I...

Mouse (USA, 1950) Launched in a V-2, this mouse was the only one to survive. The Americans subsequently sent up many mice which weren't so lucky.

Tsygan and Desik the dogs (USSR, 1951) The first dogs in space (but not in orbit) and in whose pawprints Laika followed six years later.

Gordo the squirrel monkey (USA, 1958) Trained by the US Navy, Gordo (pictured) survived the 10g-force launch, eight minutes of weightlessness and the 40g re-entry at 10,000mph, but then his parachute broke and he sank somewhere in the Atlantic.

Able and Baker (USA, 1959) The first monkeys to survive spaceflight. In all, 32 monkeys have gone into space.

Ham the chimp (USA, 1961) Trained to pull levers to receive rewards of banana pellets and proved that tasks could be completed in space.

Parasitic wasps, flour beetles and frog eggs (USA, 1966-67) Sent up in Biosatellite 1 and 2.

Horsfield's tortoise (USSR, 1968) First tortoise in space – and the first animal in deep space, as he went around the Moon.

Arabella and Anita and a Mummichog (USA, 1972) The first spiders and fish in space rode in Skylab 3, accompanied by pocket mice.

Carl Sagan

(b. 9 November 1934; d. 20 December 1996)
Astronomer

Carl Edward Sagan, a Brooklyn-born Ivy League lecturer with a PhD in astrophysics and astronomy, was the key motivator in the widescale search for extraterrestrial life. He was involved from the earliest days of the US space programme, advising Nasa and devising experiments to be carried out onboard its various missions. He also made many uncannily accurate speculations about our solar system that were later shown to be true: that Venus' atmosphere is extremely dry and hot, that the moons Titan and Europa have oceans, and that Mars changed colour because of windstorms on its surface.

> *"In order to make an apple pie from scratch, you must first create the universe.*
> Carl Sagan

Perhaps his most long-lasting legacy, however, was persuading Nasa to carry messages on its missions intended for intelligent extraterrestrial life. The first of these was a gold plaque on the Pioneer 10 mission of 1972, which depicted the chemical symbol for hydrogen, a naked man and woman, the position of the Sun in our galaxy and a schematic of our solar system. His interest in scouring the universe for other forms of life was crystallised in 1982 when he encouraged 70 eminent scientists to co-sign a letter to the journal *Nature* making the case for SETI (Search for Extraterrestrial Intelligence), an organisation which sends out signals through radio telescopes, laser beams and numerous other media just in case someone out there is listening.

Sagan also co-founded the Planetary Society, a group with more than 1 million members worldwide that promotes exploration of the solar system and the search for extraterrestrial life. He popularised the science of space in his hit US TV series *Cosmos*, and his novel *Contact* was made into a successful film starring Jodie Foster in 1997.

Look to the skies

Observatories

Today's observatories are hi-tech affairs, but it wasn't always that way. Before the invention of the telescope, an observatory was simply a well-placed vantage point – with a sextant (a measuring instrument) if you were very fortunate. Angkor Wat, Abu Simbel and even Stonehenge have all been described as early observatories used by the ancients to measure the heavens.

What changed all that was the invention of the telescope by Hans Lippershey and Jacob Metius (independently of each other) in the early 1600s and improved upon by the likes of Galileo, Kepler and Newton. Modern telescopes fall into two main categories: optical telescopes (similar to those you can buy on the high street, only slightly bigger and run by supercomputers) and radio telescopes (which track data from satellites and space probes, and are used in radio astronomy). Different types are used in different parts of the world: optical telescopes work best in dry, high altitude areas with as many clear nights and as little light pollution as possible, while radio telescopes have to avoid all electromagnetic interference, most commonly produced by radios, televisions and radar.

Maragheh, Iran Built in the 13th century, it quickly became the most influential in the world, helping to cement the Islamic empire's position at the forefront of medieval science.

Arecibo, Puerto Rico The largest single-aperture radio telescope ever constructed (305m). It featured in the James Bond film *Goldeneye*.

Jodrell Bank, Macclesfield, UK Contains the 76.2m-diameter Lovell radio telescope, once the largest in the world, which was used to track Sputnik 1's movements back in 1957.

Mauna Kea, Hawaii, USA This dormant volcano – the best site for optical observations – has 12 telescopes, with four more planned.

Roque de los Muchachos, La Palma, Canary Islands In July 2007 the £88 million Great Canary Telescope was unveiled. Its 34ft-wide mirror makes it one of the largest telescopes ever constructed.

Rocket science

How a space pioneer became an occultist

In the early decades of the 20th century the idea of space travel was deemed a childish lunacy: no universities taught it, no textbooks mentioned it. Finding his inspiration in science-fiction stories, a teenage John Whiteside Parsons (1914-52), completely self-taught, began building and launching rockets in the back garden of his Los Angeles home. It was Jack Parsons' romantic yearning to explore outer space that helped kick-start the American space programme.

Wangling his way into using the facilities of the renowned California Institute of Technology, Parsons was soon joined by a motley crew of similarly space-obsessed amateurs who swiftly became known as the Suicide Squad because of the frequency with which their rocketry experiments exploded. Yet at the same time that Parsons was building a new science, he was also exploring even stranger paths. He had become fascinated by a cult devoted to the teachings of the English occultist Aleister Crowley, known as the 'wickedest man in the world'. Soon Parsons became the group's indefatigable leader.

In 1944, Parsons founded the Jet Propulsion Laboratory, now the world's pre-eminent institution for the exploration of the solar system. Yet his private life began to spill into his professional one. He began chanting pagan poetry at rocket tests and rumours of satanic orgies swirled around him. He befriended the sci-fi writer and future founder of Scientology, L Ron Hubbard, who then ran off with Parsons' girlfriend and life savings.

By the late Forties Parsons' occult excesses were under FBI investigation and he was squeezed out of the very science he had helped create. When he died at the age of 37 in a mysterious explosion in his home laboratory, no one knew whether it was an accident, a suicide or a murder, although his friends in the science-fiction community whispered of an arcane magical ritual gone horribly, horribly wrong. GEORGE PENDLE

George Pendle is the author of Strange Angel: The Otherworldly Life of Rocket Scientist John Whiteside Parsons

Nice view

The Hubble telescope

Launched into Earth orbit in 1990 by the Space Shuttle, the Hubble Space Telescope (pictured) has provided astronomers, and the public, with views of the universe of unprecedented clarity and drama. The collision of Comet Shoemaker-Levy 9 with Jupiter in 1994 was photographed by the telescope, while its stunning shots of the Eagle and Ant nebulae, and of distant star fields, have become some of the most popular scientific images ever recorded.

The telescope, named after the US astronomer Edwin Hubble, is relatively small compared to instruments in ground-based observatories. Its primary mirror is 2.4 metres in diameter. Many ground telescopes now have mirrors that are between 8m to 10m in diameter. However, the Hubble's orbit above Earth's atmosphere gives it a unique advantage over these instruments because its images are not blurred by the atmosphere. The Hubble can also observe ultraviolet light, which is normally absorbed by the atmosphere.

The key to the success of the Hubble lies with its extremely steady and accurate pointing mechanisms. The telescope can lock onto a target without deviating more than 7/1,000th of an arcsecond from it – the width of a human hair seen at a distance of 1 mile. It is the equivalent of shining a steady laser light on a 1p coin 200 miles away.

More than 4,000 scientific papers have been published using data from the Hubble. However, scientists point out that this information was gained at an enormous price. The instrument cost $1.5 billion (£737 million) to build and it has required four servicing missions by Shuttle astronauts, with a fifth and final flight planned for September next year. The cost of each of these flights works out at around $500m (£246m) a flight. **Robin McKie**

Robin McKie is science correspondent for The Observer

What is...

The Moon

Satellites are objects that orbit a planet – the Moon (pictured) is the Earth's natural satellite (as opposed to the artificial satellites we have sent into orbit). There are more than 100 moons in our solar system and new ones are being discovered every year as interplanetary probes continue to survey the solar system in greater and greater detail. Not all planets have them, however: Mars has two small ones, Phobos and Deimos, whereas Mercury and Venus have none. Our Moon is the fifth-largest in the solar system and makes a complete orbit around the Earth every 27.3 days.

The Moon consists of an outer crust, a mantle, and a core. This structure is believed to have resulted from the fractional crystallization of a magma ocean shortly after its formation about 4.5 billion years ago. The crust is composed primarily of oxygen, silicon, magnesium, iron, calcium, and aluminium.

The Moon's gravitational force is responsible for our ocean tides and pulls the water towards it putting the oceans in constant motion and creating two high tides and two low tides each day.

A 'blue moon' is the term used to denote the second full Moon that occurs within a given calendar month. Because it takes the Moon about 29 days to orbit the Earth, it is possible that two full Moons can occur within the same calendar month, but on average this only happens once every 2.5 years. Making them rare events and giving rise to the expression 'once in a blue moon'.

The best time to view it is during a half-Moon. Near the terminator – the line of shadow – is the clearest place to see the craters, waterless seas, mountains, valleys, hills and domes as they are thrown into sharp relief. **Robin McKie**

Lunacy and other myths

How outer space has affected the way we think

Although the gravitational pull of the Moon affects the tides, could it also lead to madness? This belief has been around for millennia, leading to the story of the werewolf and giving us the word lunacy (from the Latin *luna*, meaning moon). It's thought this link exists because people suffering from certain cyclical psychological conditions, such as bipolar disorder, may have suffered sleep deprivation on particularly bright nights before the advent of street lighting, exacerbating their condition and possibly inducing mania.

Every few years, studies are published linking a full Moon with everything from violence to car crashes and even election results (one scientist suggests President Bush won the 2000 election because the electorate was more alert and rational due to the lack of a full Moon, although he may have been a Republican). Sussex police force even made a link in 2007 when it published a report noting a higher number of violent incidents in Brighton on a full Moon and promised more police officers on the streets during these lunar events.

Cosmic folklore

Northern lights Point Barrow Eskimos considered the eerie glow of the northern lights (Aurora Borealis) to be a great evil spirit, and would carry knives to protect themselves from it.

Man in the Moon The Oto Native Americans believed there was a man in the Moon. The story goes that a smitten young warrior, Running Antelope, was chased to the edge of a lake by his village chief, who wanted Running Antelope's wife for himself. At the edge of the lake the warrior asked the water spirits to save him, and they quickly shot him onto the Moon with a jet of water.

The heavens above The Aztecs believed that the visible celestial bodies were gods. The Sun itself was formed when Nanahuatl and Tecciztecatl were told by the creator gods to sacrifice themselves in a great fire. Tecciztecatl, however, chickened out, leaving Nanahuatl to become the Sun, while he became the Moon. The 1,600 other gods then agreed to sacrifice themselves to create the stars.

Virtual reality

Space for everyone

Space may be the final frontier, but for most it's a pretty abstract concept – little more than some stars glimpsed on a dark night. Actually participating in space exploration has been unthinkable... until now. Thanks to the internet, it is now possible to boldly go where no one has gone before. Nasa is currently experimenting with ways to get the public more involved in future exploration of the Moon, Mars and other destinations in the solar system, particularly through the use of virtual-reality tools. Here's how you can launch yourself into it without donning a spacesuit...

Nasa gets a Second Life

Nasa's best-known foray into the virtual world is its presence in *Second Life*, an online digital world developed by Linden Lab. Its residents – 7.6 million at last count, from more than 100 real-life countries – own and build the virtual world's digital infrastructure, including houses, museums, nightclubs, islands, companies and so on.

Nasa's Collaborative Space Exploration Laboratory (CoLab) has its own 'island' in *Second Life*, a virtual interactive-learning community where anyone interested in space travel or technology can explore and contribute to the space agency's mission. The nearby Explorer Island – with its spacecraft, exhibits, interactive displays, Mars rovers, meeting spaces and public events – offers a new way to increase global participation in Nasa's exploration agenda.

The objective is for the islands to become a portal through which everyone can hitch a lift on future space missions: real data from real missions such as the International Space Station can be viewed in this virtual environment – and it's hoped that in the future, users will be able to actually take part virtually alongside scientists and engineers managing the mission.

Google Moon, July 2005

A lunar-mapping platform embedded with panoramic images, links to audio clips and videos, and descriptions of the astronauts' activities during the Apollo Moon landings, all overlaid on high-resolution lunar maps.

Google Mars, March 2006

Allows you to explore the red planet in three ways: there's an elevation map showing peaks and valleys, a visible-imagery map showing what you would see were you to stand on its surface, and an infrared-imagery map showing the detail your eyes would miss.

Google Sky, August 2007

An updated version of Google Earth with a new service called Sky that allows users to view the heavens as seen from Earth. Like Google Earth, Sky lets users fly around and zoom in, exposing increasingly detailed imagery of some 100m stars and 200m galaxies stitched together from more than 1m photographs from scientific and academic sources, including the Sloan Digital Sky Survey, the Palomar Observatory at the California Institute of Technology and the Nasa-financed Hubble Space Telescope. Sky already has layers showing various constellations, a user's guide to galaxies, the position of planets two months into the future, and animations of lunar positions. A 'backyard astronomy' layer highlights stars, galaxies and nebulae that are visible to the naked eye with binoculars or with small telescopes.

Pippi Longstocking in space

In 1995 the Swedes launched the ASTRID 1 microsatellite. Originally named Astrid simply because it was a common, old-fashioned Swedish name, it shortly became viewed as an homage to Astrid Lindgren, author of the Pippi Longstocking books – standard reading for Swedish children. The instruments were named after characters in the books, so the neural particle imager gained the much more friendly name Pippi, the electron spectrometer Emil, and the miniature UV imaging system became Mio. Designed to last a year, the instruments failed after just three months.

The Observer archive: historic moments in space exploration

The drama of Apollo 13

(13 April 1970)

All over the world – except imaginably in China and in those vast regions too poor for television – people are relaxing this weekend after the stresses of a unique human emergency.

Predominant among our emotions must be the relief that washed over us as Apollo 13, with millions watching it, floated safely down in a kind of dream sequence through the woolly Pacific clouds tinged orange by the propellants jettisoned from the spacecraft.

Heads of governments sent their messages, church bells rang in small American towns, brokers applauded on the Paris stock exchange, motor horns honked in Brazil, sirens blew in Milan, gamblers left the tables of Las Vegas long enough to see the happy ending, with helpful Russian missile-tracking ships and whalers racing towards the splashdown. ...

Behind the general relief there lies a feeling of bafflement. Contradictions spring to mind:

1 Instruments at the Houston Control Center were of such sensitivity that they could register an astronaut's heartbeat thousands of miles away in space. But the Apollo 13 could lose a panel 13 feet long without the scale of the disaster being even roughly detected until a surprised astronaut saw the discarded service module floating away.

2 At this dismaying sight, he did not express a reasonable extremity of fear. The dialogue went thus:

Lovell: And there's one whole side of the spacecraft missing.

Control: Is that right?

Lovell: Right by the high-gain antenna. The whole panel is blown out.

Control: Copy that.

3 It was a truly exhausting mission – days of little or no sleep, of cold and the presence of fear – and the viewer expects human beings to step out of the capsule registering this experience. Instead, they

stepped jauntily onto the deck of the aircraft carrier like distinguished guests arriving at a convention.

4 After such an immense voyage, beside which that of Columbus seems in terms of distance a mere jaunt, the capsule splashed down within four miles of the chosen target and within five seconds of the forecast time. Yet at another point in the flight its survival seemed to depend on the Boy Scout improvisation of an air pump from a urine bag and some sticking-plaster.

In its very nature, the Apollo 13 emergency was unique in the history of man. The first news of it was enough to transform public reaction to the whole project. Until it happened people had been bewildered by their own boredom, their inability to take an interest in something that ought surely to have gripped them. Even American television had switched away from the spacecraft's progress and started showing the usual old films as something less tedious. But then came the news flash – 'Hey, we have a problem' – and at once the attention of the world was gripped. Before long, here in Britain the *Daily Express* was exhorting us to pray. ...

We do not need to speculate too broadly about the kind of death the astronauts would have died. This weekend they might have been dying of lack of oxygen, moving more and more slowly, sweating heavily, feeling intense claustrophobia, losing the capacity for rational thought, perhaps having bouts of insanity interrupted by moments of peaceful contentment. Or they might have died from carbon-dioxide poisoning. One of the survivors of the Thetis submarine – which sank with the loss of 99 lives in 1939, still remembers with great clarity the symptoms of vomiting and headaches and the feeling of drowsiness and the way 'men began just to lie down and go to sleep.'

Given these alternative endings, the scale of the universal relief does not seem exaggerated. The father of [command module pilot John] Swigert spoke for all of us when he said, in that brief moment of general delight at splashdown: 'It was a wonderful beginning and a beautiful ending. But I wouldn't give you two hoots for the interim.'

William Millinship and Cyril Dunn, 19 April 1970

APOLLO 13

Saga of man's most dangerous journey

DAYLIGHT

Bewildered by their boredom

'Only one thing for us to do'

Valentina Tereshkova

(b. 6 March 1937)
Cosmonaut

Valentina Vladimirovna Tereshkova became the first woman, and the first civilian, in space in June 1963 when Vostok 6 took her into Earth's orbit for three days. She remained in orbit for longer than all of Nasa's Mercury astronauts combined.

An expert parachutist and secretary of her local Communist Youth League, Tereshkova was chosen ahead of far more qualified candidates at the behest of Russian leader Khrushchev himself. Soviet command had already decided that a Vostok spacecraft would be sent up on autopilot and their only requirement was that a 'likable' Communist girl who knew how to parachute down once the craft re-entered the atmosphere was sent.

> “*If women can be railroad workers in Russia, why can't they fly in space?*
> Valentina Tereshkova

Her commanders' mistrust of a female cosmonaut only became apparent once the mission was in progress. Tereshkova was sick early in the flight, a problem which she later revealed to be due to the appalling food, but which Ground Control blamed on 'space sickness'. Because of this, they forced her to remain strapped into her seat for the rest of the three-day voyage. More distressingly, bad calculations left the craft incorrectly orientated for re-entry – a mistake that could have killed Tereshkova had she not argued with the disbelieving ground crew. When she landed she was chastised for disobeying direct orders. It took another 29 years after Tereshkova's landmark flight for the next woman to reach space.

On her return, she became a national hero and married fellow cosmonaut Yuliy Shaposhnikov with whom she had a daughter (their union is surrounded by rumours of a propaganda marriage). They divorced in 1982. She continues to work with international women's organisations to this day.

Ten famous aliens

The alien (*Alien*, 1979) A living weapon that, despite its fearsome yet intelligent reputation, has one of the worst showbiz agents in the solar system. *Alien vs Predator*? Really?

Barbarella (pictured) **(*Barbarella*, 1968)** The adventures of this 41st-century astronaut take her to the planet Lythion, where she survives the evil professor Durand Durand and a potentially fatal orgasm on the Excessive Machine, all the time contending with clothes that just won't stay on.

The blob (*The Blob*, 1958) Riding meteors through the solar system, this little jelly thing kills literally tens of people.

The Daleks (*Doctor Who*, from 2005) Created by the brilliant, yet mad, scientist Davros out of some old bins on the mysterious planet Skaro. They quickly exterminate him and spread themselves about the galaxy, bringing nothing but doom... and ramps.

ET (*ET*, 1982) Travels round the galaxy befriending young boys while pointing a lot. Loves *Sesame Street*.

Space vampires (*Lifeforce*, 1985) Originally from Halley's comet, these evil – yet in one unlikely case exotically beautiful – spacebeings turn most of London's population into zombies.

Spock (*Star Trek*, from 1966) Half Vulcan (who can never tell lies), half man (who can, which sometimes leads to all kinds of sticky situations), Spock is a clever, reserved sort who apparently represents the human brain's intellect (Kirk is the ego, while Dr McCoy is the id).

Superman (*Superman*, from 1978) He can fly, shoot heat from his eyes, see through things, freeze things with his breath; he's invincible, strong and also holds down a job as a mild-mannered reporter.

The thing (*The Thing*, 1982) It can shapeshift into anything, but seems to choose the form of an ugly monster.

Yoda (*Star Wars*, from 1977) According to the lore of the Jedi, Yoda is the definitive master of the martial art Ataru and can deflect Force Lightning. He is, however, only the second best in the galaxy with a lightsabre, behind Tulak Horde.

Six celebrity UFO spotters

1 Muhammad Ali Regularly witnessed UFOs and was reported as saying: 'If you look into the sky in the early morning, you see them playing tag between the stars.'

2 David Bowie The Thin White Duke once worked for two guys who put out a UFO magazine. 'I made sightings six, seven times a night for about a year when I was in the observatory,' he once said. 'We had regular cruises that came over.'

3 Jimmy Carter The former US president saw a UFO while he was the governor of Virginia. On 6 January 1969 he saw a light which appeared 'bluish at first, then reddish, luminous, not solid. It appeared as bright as the moon.' Of the event he said: 'I was with 20 other men and we saw a bright light in the sky. It got closer, and when it was just above the trees it changed colour. I still don't know what it was.' Experts believe he misidentified the planet Venus.

4 Jimi Hendrix He once told a reporter from the *New York Times* that he was really from Mars. After his Rainbow Bridge concert in Hawaii, witnesses claimed they heard musical tones emanating from rocks and stones, UFOs were sighted over the volcano by people who called in to a local radio show, and an on-set cameraman said that he fell from his perch after seeing a UFO through his lens.

5 Elvis Presley Strange lights appeared in the sky at the time Elvis was born and one was reportedly seen hovering over the mourners when his coffin was interred in the grounds of Graceland. Some even speculate that perhaps The King himself was an extraterrestrial and not in the coffin at all but looking down from the flying saucer.

6 William Shatner Fittingly, the *Star Trek* actor claimed to have been saved by an alien who showed him the way before flying off in a 'shining orb-shaped object that was hovering in the sky' after he crashed his motorcycle in the Mojave Desert.

Alien abduction

The truth is out there...

While the concept of alien abduction did not enter the public consciousness until the Sixties, cases with all the familiar characteristics have been documented as far back as the 1800s. In 1897 Colonel HG Shaw described in Stockton, California's *Daily Mail* how he and his friend fought off three tall, slender humanoids covered with fine, downy hair that were trying to accost or kidnap them.

In 1961 the first widely publicised abduction case emerged in America. While driving home, Betty and Barney Hill lost two hours after sighting a pancake-shaped aircraft. During subsequent hypnosis, they individually described being abducted by aliens and being shown around the spacecraft before undergoing medical examinations. These characteristics have since been reproduced in numerous other accounts from fellow 'experiencers'.

Encounters include being paralysed by some unknown force, and being examined and probed by a number of large-eyed, grey-skinned, hairless creatures. Tissues and cells are then sampled and subcutaneous implants are often installed. The abductees are then returned with no memory of the encounter.

Have you been abducted?

There are those who believe that, absurd as it may sound, millions of people across the world have been abducted by aliens without knowing it. The New York based Roper Organization polls a sample population each year for its Limobus survey. Working closely with abduction therapists, American property billionaire and pioneer in alien abduction Robert Bigelow inserted specially devised questions, among the more innocuous queries about preferred sweetness of ketchup and so on, into three Limobus surveys to learn the number and character of alien abductees. In 1992, a representative sample of about 6,000 American adults showed that one in 50 met the profile of an abductee, suggesting that 1.7% of the American population has been abducted. A surprisingly large number of these people fall into a category termed 'influentials' – those aged 35 to 45 who have higher-than-average incomes and are in positions of authority.

Contact

Take the alien abduction questionnaire

Could you have been abducted by aliens? Have you experienced loss of time or strange, unaccountable markings on your skin? Do you relive confused visions of other worlds or strange beings? If any of this feels familiar, you could have been abducted by aliens. Answer the following questions, taken from the Limobus survey (see previous page), to discover the truth...

1 Do you spend long periods of time in the garden? ❑ Yes ❑ No

2 Have you ever experienced an odd displacement in which you found yourself inexplicably in a location different from where you remember being only seconds before and it was not the common 'road hypnosis' while driving?
❑ Yes ❑ No

3 As a child or an adult, did you ever experience any lost periods of time you cannot account for?
❑ Yes ❑ No

4 Do you have any scars or marks on your body that you can't remember receiving?
❑ Yes ❑ No

5 Have you ever woken up paralysed, with the sense of a person, presence or something else in the room? ❑ Yes ❑ No

6 Have you ever seen lights or balls of light in your room for which you have no explanation?
❑ Yes ❑ No

7 Have you ever felt that you were actually and inexplicably flying, and it was not an out-of-body experience or a dream? ❑ Yes ❑ No

8 Do you have inexplicable fears about certain areas such as stretches of highway, open fields, rooms in a house and so forth? ❑ Yes ❑ No

9 Do you remember having seen, either as a child or an adult, a terrifying figure – which might have been a monster, a witch, a devil or some other evil figure – in your bedroom or closet or somewhere else? ❑ Yes ❑ No

10 Have you actually left your body, or had an unwanted and/or unexpected out-of-body experience? ❑ Yes ❑ No

11 Has a deceased relative or friend ever visited you in your home at night? ❑ Yes ❑ No

12 Have you ever seen, or sensed the presence of, a ghost?
❑ Yes ❑ No

13 Have you ever awakened wearing clothes that were not yours and you did not know how you got them, and/or have you ever awakened with your clothes on in the wrong way or not on at all when you had put them on correctly? ❑ Yes ❑ No

14 Have you recently been inspired to save the world from ecological disaster? ❑ Yes ❑ No

How did you do?

If you answered Yes to 1-4 questions It is unlikely that you have been abducted by aliens. But this is no guarantee that they haven't earmarked you for the future.

If you answered Yes to 5-9 questions There is a possibility that you have been abducted by aliens or have been chosen for abduction in the future.

If you answered Yes to 10-14 questions CONGRATULATIONS! It is extremely likely that you have been abducted by aliens. You have been chosen from among 6.5 billion people on Earth by aliens wishing to make contact with humans. Since aliens are thought to abduct chosen individuals repeatedly, it is also highly likely that you may be abducted by aliens again in the future.

The insider: space minister

Ian Pearson

Space has transformed our way of life. We have a vibrant space industry here in the UK: we've participated in the European Space Agency (ESA), we are world leaders when it comes to robotic exploration, and this is a growing industry. Revenues are growing 15% per year in satellite communications and navigation, and it's clearly an important industry for the future, providing thousands of highly skilled jobs in the UK.

I've got no doubt that in five, 10 or 20 years' time, space is going to be even more important than it is today, and we need to reflect that in government policy. Obviously there's talk of what the programme might be like in 20 years, and certainly I want to see a UK space community that's at the forefront of space exploration, as well as a growth of highly skilled, creative people working together on space systems. It really is, I think, part of our future, and critical to our national infrastructure.

We shouldn't forget Britain's position at the forefront of robotics and remote spaceflight. I was at Jodrell Bank in October 2007 to mark the 50th anniversary of Sputnik 1, and I spoke to a professor who was using some of the designs of Beagle 2 to develop a portable mass spectrometer that could be used to help people with TB in the developing world. Some things are pretty certain to happen in the future – instant communications, access to staggering amounts of information – through the technology of space programmes, but there are also space applications that have had an impact on healthcare.

We're developing a space strategy, which I hope to launch (excuse the pun) by the end of 2007, and I'm keen for us to be fully engaged in global space-exploration programmes. There's no doubt that the world will be looking to return to the Moon and to reach other planets in our solar system. We need to look carefully at what the UK's role in that international endeavour is going to be. We will continue to be a part of ESA, and to develop partnerships with Nasa and Russia. Space exploration is costly and hugely resource intensive. Going it alone isn't a sensible strategy.

Certainly revenues are growing at the moment. The UK is home to the world's most profitable global mobile-communications provider, the Mars Aerostationary Relay Satellite (MarSat), and the world's leading small satellite company, Surrey Satellite Technology (SSTL). The key issue for me is to make sure we think long term about where we're going to devote our energies. Will there be a Briton on the Moon? If we're thinking 20 years into the future, we definitely shouldn't rule that out. In 50 years maybe we'll have a British embassy on the Moon... **Ian Pearson**

Ian Pearson is MP for Dudley South and minister for science and innovation

What are...

Solar, lunar and total eclipses

Eclipses can occur only when the Sun, Earth and Moon are all lined up. Solar eclipses occur when the Moon passes in front of the Sun and its shadow falls on the Earth. In contrast, lunar eclipses occur at full Moon, when the Earth is between the Sun and Moon and the shadow of the Earth falls on the Moon.

During a total eclipse (pictured), the Moon completely covers the disc of the Sun, and the solar corona (the glowing atmosphere around the Sun that extends millions of kilometres out into space) becomes visible to the naked eye.

An annular eclipse occurs when the Moon is at its maximum distance from the Earth and so its disc does not completely cover the Sun, producing a golden ring. It is called an annular eclipse after *annulus*, which is Latin for ring, not because it occurs annually. **Robin McKie**

Amazing stories

A brief history of science fiction

Although the term science fiction was not coined until 1929, features of the genre stretch back to antiquity. Many rank Plato's description of Atlantis as the first example of what would become a perennial science-fiction staple: the advanced, but lost, society. Other sci-fi traits can be seen in Thomas More's novel *Utopia* (1515), the inspiration for countless impossibly perfect (and dystopian) lands – and Johannes Kepler's 1634 *Somnium* (*The Dream*) was the first book to mention the possibility of travelling into outer space.

> "*Everything is becoming science fiction. From the margins of an almost invisible literature has sprung the intact reality of the 20th century.*
>
> JG Ballard

Yet the two authors to whom all modern science fiction is indebted are Jules Verne and HG Wells. While Verne described the technicalities of his scientific adventures in great detail, never veering far from known science, Wells painted his imagined innovations in broad strokes, preferring to stress the moral conundrums man faced in the technological age.

The increasing interest in scientific romances led Hugo Gernsback, an inventor and marketer of radio sets, to begin publishing the first pulp magazine, *Amazing Stories*, in 1926. Gernsback shared with Verne and Wells a Victorian enthusiasm for scientific progress. He labelled the genre 'scientifiction' and encouraged stories that would both astound and educate his largely adolescent readership.

By the late Thirties and early Forties, science fiction had entered its golden age. *Astounding Science Fiction* magazine, under the editorship of the physicist John W Campbell, contained stories by such up-and-coming writers as Ray Bradbury, Robert A Heinlein and Isaac Asimov. It was Campbell's earnest desire that science fiction should be a prophetic medium, inspiring and presaging new technological breakthroughs. Such was the quality of *Astounding*'s stories that throughout the Second World War, Wernher von Braun, head of the German V-2 rocket programme, had copies air-dropped to him in neutral Sweden. **George Pendle**

 Top five predictions of science fiction

1 The Apollo Moon landing In his story 'From the Earth to the Moon' (1865), Jules Verne spoke of three astronauts being sent to the Moon in a projectile which had almost exactly the same dimensions and weight of the Apollo Command Module that was launched from Florida before an eventual ocean landing and recovery by a US Navy ship. Admittedly Verne thought the astronauts would be fired into space out of a 900ft-long cannon. Even so, that cannon was named Columbiad. The Apollo Command Module was named Columbia.

2 The atomic bomb In his story 'The World Set Free' (1914), HG Wells wrote of the incredible destruction of 'atomic bombs', fuelled by a substance that was so small it could be carried about 'in a handbag' and which 'any little body of malcontents could use'. In the story, the atomic bombs are invented in 1933. Leo Szilard, the founder of the Manhattan Project, read the book in 1932. He would conceive of the idea of a nuclear chain reaction in 1933.

3 Organ transplants W Alexander's story 'New Stomachs for Old', which appeared in the pulp science-fiction magazine *Amazing Stories* in 1927, prophesied the concept of organ transplants other than skin grafts. But it was Larry Niven, in *The Long Arm of Gil Hamilton* (1976), who first suggested the idea of organ legging – the theft of human body parts for resale.

4 Satellites Edward Everett Hale first came up with the idea of an artificial satellite in his short story 'The Brick Moon' (1869). The idea of geosynchronous satellites as telecommunications relays was proposed by science-fiction author Arthur C Clarke in 1945 but in a scientific paper rather than a story. The geostationary orbit is now known as the Clarke Belt in his honour.

5 Aerial warfare HG Wells' *The War in the Air* (1907) envisioned legions of German airships and airplanes embarking on mass-bombing campaigns. The book also describes Russia as being torn apart by revolution, tensions between Japan and the United States, and the reluctance of both Italy and France to fight. Wells would also predict the use of the tank in his story 'The Land Ironclads' in 1903. **George Pendle**

Gene Roddenberry

(b. 19 August 1921; d. 24 October 1991)

Star Trek *creator*

The son of a Los Angeles policeman, Eugene Wesley 'Gene' Roddenberry trained as a pilot and was awarded the Distinguished Flying Cross for his B-17 bomber missions in the Pacific during the Second World War. After the war he became a commercial pilot and was commended for his actions when his Pan Am flight from Calcutta to Karachi came down in the Syrian desert. In his late twenties he returned to LA to writ but became a policeman to pay the bills.

It was his 1964 brainchild *Star Trek* (originally entitled 'Wagon Train to the Stars') that won him universal fame and promoted a popular vision of man in space. It allowed Roddenberry to tackle issues such as racism, imperialism and violence with the buffer of being set 200 years in the future.

> "Star Trek *speaks to some basic human needs that the human race is improving, that we have things to be proud of as humans.*
>
> Gene Roddenberry

Although *Star Trek* was axed after three series of low ratings, reruns began to gain a cult following and in 1975 the first *Star Trek* movie was made. With further series (there have been 726 episodes and 10 films in all) *Star Trek* became the biggest TV success of all time: Klingon, the language of an alien race in the show, is now taught at Oregon University and Nasa's first space shuttle was named *Enterprise* after the programme's starship.

In 1997, a thumb-sized capsule containing some of Roddenberry's ashes was launched into space. An asteroid and an impact crater on Mars have both been named in Roddenberry's honour and Nasa cited his 'distinguished service to the nation and the human race in presenting the exploration of space as an exciting frontier' when it posthumously awarded him a Distinguished Public Service Medal.

Moontalkers

The wit and wisdom of astronauts

Michael Collins, the Command Module pilot for the Apollo 11 mission that put the first men on the Moon, once remarked that 'what the space programme needs is more English majors'. Suddenly confronted by the profound beauty and awe-inspiring vastness of the universe, astronauts struggled to describe what they could see as these extracts from the lunar journals of the Apollo missions show...

Alan Bean, Apollo 12, en route

It [the Earth] just sort of hangs out there in this black space, and the Moon just doesn't seem to be any bigger than it was when we left, but it looks more like a sphere also. It sort of looks like a ball that is being hung out there somehow. It's really crazy.

Dave Scott, Apollo 15, before landing

It's just absolutely overwhelming... it's hard for the mental computer to sort it all out and give it back to you. I hope over the next few days we can sort of get our minds organised and get a little more precise on what we're seeing. But I'll tell you: this is absolutely mind-boggling up here.

Dave Scott, Apollo 15, on the surface

As I stand out here in the wonders of the unknown at Hadley, I sort of realise there's a fundamental truth to our nature. Man must explore. And this is exploration at its greatest.

Gene Cernan, Apollo 17, before leaving

As I take man's last step from the surface, back home for some time to come – but, we believe, not too long into the future – I'd like to just (say) what I believe history will record. That America's challenge of today has forged man's destiny of tomorrow. And as we leave the Moon at Taurus-Littrow, we leave as we came – and, God willing, as we shall return – with peace and hope for all mankind. Godspeed the crew of Apollo 17.

Space food

Space rations have come a long way since the freeze-dried 'matter' the early pioneers had to endure. Now astronauts in the International Space Station (ISS) can choose from more than 50 carefully prepared meals (including vegan and international options). The freeze-dried packets are still there – it's the best way to minimise weight – but they are balanced with packaged food that has been either thermostabilised (nuked under intense heat) or irradiated and supplemented with nuts, biscuits and occasional fruit and veg.

Meals must be carefully balanced. Astronauts produce fewer red blood cells in space than they do on Earth, so iron is included sparingly (too much in the bloodstream can prove dangerous). Vitamin D, however, is a must. The spacecraft's shields block all sunlight, protecting the crew from harmful radiation, but also limiting the body's ability to produce the vitamin.

Space can also have a funny effect on the taste buds, so more than 15 varieties of condiment, including liquid salt and pepper and a vast array of hot sauces, are included. In place of bread (too many crumbs, it seems) astronauts eat tortillas. And to deal with microgravity, most meals involve some sort of sauce so that the food sticks to the cutlery – soup is a favourite, but the most popular meal is Shrimp Cocktail.

The menus

Apollo 11 (1969)

Meal A
Bacon Squares, Peaches, Sugar Cookie Cubes, Coffee, Pineapple-Grapefruit Drink

Meal B
Beef Stew, Cream of Chicken Soup, Date Fruitcake, Grape Punch, Orange Drink

Note: Astronauts alternated between Meal A and Meal B

ISS (2007)

Breakfast
Rice Krispies, Cinnamon Roll, Pears, Vanilla Breakfast Drink, Kona Coffee with Cream and Sugar, Earl Grey Tea with Sugar

Lunch
Teriyaki Chicken, Macaroni and Cheese, Rice Pilaf, Macadamia Nuts, Grapefruit Drink

Dinner
Shrimp Cocktail, Beef Tips with Mushrooms, Pasta with Herbs, Butterscotch Pudding, Strawberry Drink, Tea with Lemon

Eating among the (Michelin) stars

In an effort to boost morale among astronauts, the CNES (French National Centre of Space Studies) and chef Richard Filippi came up with the idea of Special Event Meals (SEMs). Renowned chefs designed and produced meals that would both fit in with the practical and dietary constraints of space travel and provide a delicious break from the freeze-dried norm.

The first to design such a gourmet space feast was New Orleans Cajun chef Emeril Lagasse in August 2006. He created spicy gumbo and jambalaya for the orbiting crew. The imperious holder of nine Michelin stars, chef Alain Ducasse followed him a few months later. Although there are plans for more SEMs in the future, Charles Simonyi, who became the fifth space tourist in April 2007, carried a special space dinner knocked up by his Earth-bound girlfriend Martha Stewart to help him settle in with his new spacemates on the ISS.

Alain Ducasse's space menu

Effiloché de volaille en Parmentier *(Shredded chicken Parmentier)*
Dos d'espadon façon Riviera *(Riviera-style swordfish)*
Volaille épicée, sauté de légumes à la Thaï *(Spicy chicken with stir-fried Thai vegetables)*
Cailles rôties au Madiran *(Quails roasted in Madiran wine)*
Magret de canard confit, condiment aux câpres *(Duck-breast 'confit' with capers)*

ꕤ

Carottes de sable au goût d'orange et coriandre *(Sand carrots with a hint of orange and coriander)*
Céleri-rave en délicate purée à la noix de muscade *(A light purée of celery with a hint of nutmeg)*
Caponata *(Tomato, aubergine and olive dip)*

ꕤ

Gâteau de semoule de blé fine aux abricots secs *(Semolina cake with dried apricots)*
Morceaux de pommes fondants *(Apple fondant pieces)*
Far de l'espace *(Space 'far' – a Brittany tart)*
Rice pudding aux fruits confits *(Rice pudding with candied fruit)*

Faked?

Apollo conspiracy theories debunked

Almost 40 years after 12 American astronauts set foot on the Moon, there are still those who don't believe they actually got there, and a number of well-worn conspiracy theories continue to be put about. Here are five, and why they're wrong...

1 The flag appears to wave, but there is no wind on the Moon

To stop the flag from hanging flat, the astronauts inserted stiff wire into the fabric to pull it taut. The 'waving' is caused by them pushing it in – after they've finished, the flag is motionless.

2 In all the photographs no stars are visible

Just as a nighttime photo taken on Earth will very rarely show stars, the brightness of nearby objects will block the light of faint, distant stars. In fact, if you were standing on the daylight side of the Moon you wouldn't even be able to see them with the naked eye.

3 The shadows in the pictures were often of different lengths and didn't run parallel to each other, proving there was more than one source of light

The pictures were taken on a hilly landscape while the Sun was close to the horizon. The contours of the ground would make the shadows take odd courses and lengths, just as they would on a snowy, uneven landscape on Earth.

4 They couldn't have taken pictures on the Moon – the film would have melted

The camera was in a reflective white case to keep the radiation out. However, without convection or conduction, radiation is the only form of heat transfer on the Moon.

5 The Apollo crews were launched into space but never left Earth's orbit

As the spacecraft entered orbit they were easily observable from Earth, even with the naked eye. Many amateur astronomers followed the capsules until the point at which they disappeared, and the Soviets tracked them all the way to the Moon.

What is...

Solar wind

Solar wind originates in the Sun's outer layer (the corona), where electrically charged particles, gathered together in a cloudy plasma, are fired from the Sun. The Earth's magnetic field – and, as a last defence, our thick atmosphere – protects us from these particles. The glow caused by these particles smashing into gases in the Earth's ionosphere is known to us as the northern lights (Aurora Borealis) and the southern lights (Aurora Australis). The array of colours in these magnificent displays consists of red, green, blue and violet and is in constant motion because of the changing interaction between the solar wind and the Earth's magnetic field. The solar wind can generate up to 1,000,000 megawatts of electricity in an auroral display.

The fact that solar winds can ruin the electronics of a satellite necessitate regular space 'weather reports', issued by the Space Environment Center. Also tracked by these reports are solar flares, violent explosions on the Sun's surface that release massive amounts of electromagnetic radiation. **Robin McKie**

Soundtrack to the stars

Larger-than-life moonwalker Pete Conrad smuggled on board Apollo 12 a tape player and cassettes of his favourite songs, which mildly irritated his fellow astronauts. Here are 10 songs he played in space...

'San Antonio Rose' by Bob Wills
'Louisiana Man' by Rusty and Doug
'Chattanooga Choo Choo' by Glenn Miller
'Can't Take My Eyes Off You' by Vikki Carr
'Wichita Lineman' by Glen Campbell
'The Girl from Ipanema' by Astrud Gilberto
'Sugar, Sugar' by the Archies
'Suspicious Minds' by Elvis Presley
'Little Woman' by Bobby Sherman
'Son of a Preacher Man' by Dusty Springfield

A heavenly refrain

The Music of the Spheres

In the 5th century BC Pythagoras had a revelation. Music, he realised, operates according to the same mathematical laws which govern the rest of the world, and indeed the cosmos. The philosopher posited that the stars and planets – 'the spheres' of the pre-Copernican universe – were part of a celestial refrain, a divine symphony. Ever since, humanity, especially musicians and astronomers, has been trying to tune in.

As celebrated in Handel's *Harmonious Blacksmith*, Pythagoras' eureka moment arrived to the sounds of hammers in a smithy's forge. He noticed that a heavy hammer produced a frequency twice as long as that produced by one half its weight, an octave lower; that the musical scale correlated with simple mathematical ratios.

'The Music of the Spheres' became a keystone of the hermetic tradition, reiterated by the likes of Plato and Ptolemy, and famously illustrated (below) by the English alchemist Robert Fludd in 1618. Fludd's scales spanned three octaves, linking base, material worlds to angelic choirs singing beyond the stars. Around the same time Johannes Kepler proved that Pythagoras's theory was astronomic fact. Kepler's laws of planetary motion showed that the orbits of the planets are elliptical rather than circular, and that a planet's speed varies at different stages of its orbit.

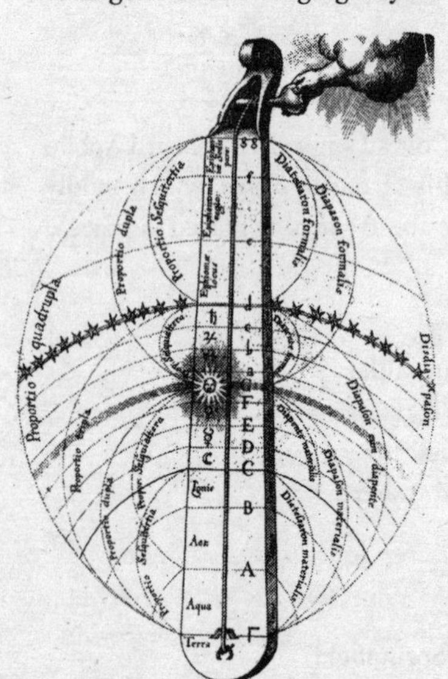

Moreover, planetary motion follows music's template. For example, the ratio between Jupiter's maximum and Mars' minimum speed corresponds to a minor third; that between Earth and Venus to a minor sixth. Even a hard-hat astronomer like Fred Hoyle concedes that the

correspondence between musical ratios and planetary velocities is 'frighteningly good'.

Kepler's discoveries confirmed that the Copernican, Sun-centred view of the solar system was correct. For Kepler they also showed the divine harmony of creation. In *Harmonia Mundi* (1619), he described 'the song which the cosmos sings to its lord and centre, the Solar Logos'. The modern age has continued to pursue the celestial refrain, mixing the quest for divine harmony with science fiction and space-age exploration. **Neil Spencer**

Five cosmic compositions

1 *The Planets* (1919) Gustav Holst
Holst, a keen theosophist, based his celebrated suite on the astrological character of planets. Titles like 'Mars, the Bringer of War' and 'Neptune, the Mystic' were lifted intact from Edwardian astrologer Alan Leo.

2 'Astronomy Domine' (1967) Pink Floyd
Before sinking into terrestrial gloom, Floyd were keen astronauts. Their debut album *The Piper At The Gates of Dawn* opened with this tour of the solar system – 'Stars can frighten' – alongside the psychedelic thrash of 'Interstellar Overdrive'. Far out, man.

3 'Third Stone from the Sun' (1967) Jimi Hendrix
Jimi was another self-styled brother from another planet, just visiting. Here he lands his 'kinky machine' on Earth to admire its 'majestic silver seas and mysterious mountains'.

4 *Space is the Place* (1972) Sun Ra
Claiming to come from Saturn, electronic pioneer Sun Ra invented 'cosmic jazz' back in the Fifties on albums like *We Travel the Spaceways*, but this is his most famous and successful evocation of the deep dark stuff.

5 *Licht* (1977-2003) Karlheinz Stockhausen
The German modernist's epic features a planetary symphony for each day of the week – Moon for Monday, Saturn for Saturday etc. Performances include stage areas allocated to planets, among which musicians move. **Neil Spencer**

The Observer archive: historic moments in space exploration

The Columbia disaster

(1 February 2003)

The space shuttle Columbia erupted in flames yesterday as it re-entered the Earth's atmosphere at 12,000mph, killing all seven crew members and plunging America into mourning and despair.

Stunned Nasa officials at Mission Control stood in front of their computers, staring silently at the screens, as TV pictures of the craft disintegrating were beamed in shortly after radio contact was lost, 16 minutes before it was due to land at Kennedy Space Center in Florida.

Last night President George W Bush confirmed during a sombre address broadcast live to the nation that all the astronauts had died. 'The Columbia is lost,' he said. 'There are no survivors.' He paid tribute to the crew: 'These men and women assumed a great risk in the service of all humanity. These astronauts knew the dangers and faced them willingly, knowing they had a high and noble purpose in life. All Americans are thinking of the families of these men and women. You are not alone: our entire nation grieves with you.' Tony Blair last night sent a message of sympathy to America.

Earlier, shocked wives, husbands and children of the astronauts, who had been waiting at the landing strip, were taken to an area away from the public gaze.

As the disaster was taking place, no word or data came from Columbia , and Mission Control repeated over and over again: 'A contingency for the space shuttle has been declared.'

Simon Garfield on the 'happy pill' that hooked the nation

The Observer

FREE SPORT MAGAZINE

NICOLE
Kidman tells all in a revealing intervie

Disaster in space

Seven astronauts die as
uttle explodes in flames
Debris rains down as craft
reaks up at 12,000mph
Bush pays tribute to crew
n address to grieving nation

As the TV pictures were flashed around the world and shocked Americans tried to take in the scale of the tragedy, people in Texas reported a 'big bang' shortly after 2pm GMT. Dramatic footage showed the shuttle ablaze and breaking up at 200,000ft. Clouds of vapour trailed along beside the craft.

The break-up could be seen and heard from the ground as the craft's single starburst gradually split into a firework of streaks. At first the starburst broke into two, each with its own plume. Then they, too, began to splinter. ...

There was speculation last night that an earlier accident on Columbia could have loosened a heat-resistant tile supposed to ensure the craft did not catch fire as a result of the friction generated by re-entering the atmosphere at high speeds.

> *Although we grieve deeply, as do the families of Apollo 1 and Challenger before us, the bold exploration of space must go on.*
>
> Joint statement from the astronauts' families

Shortly after Columbia lifted off two weeks ago, a piece of insulating foam on its external fuel tank came off. It was believed to have struck the left wing of the shuttle, possibly loosening the tile. Leroy Cain, the lead flight director in Mission Control, gave assurances hours before the explosion that engineers had concluded that any damage was considered minor and posed no safety hazard.

But last night Nasa officials revealed they now believed the damage to the wing could have been crucial. 'We cannot discount that there might be a connection,' said Ron Dittemore, head of the shuttle programme. He revealed that an hour before the disaster, transmission of data from hydraulics sensors – sited on the left wing – stopped abruptly. 'It was as if someone had cut a wire,' Dittemore said. The astronauts were not told of the problem. ...

It was almost 17 years to the day since the last major space shuttle disaster. The Challenger shuttle exploded on 28 January 1986, also killing all seven astronauts on board. Columbia, Nasa's oldest shuttle, first flew in 1981. ...

Michael Anderson, one of the Columbia astronauts, said in an interview before the fateful trip: 'When you launch in a rocket, you're not really flying that rocket. You're just sort of hanging on. You're taking an explosion and you're trying to control it. You're trying to harness that energy to propel you into space. We're very successful in doing that. But there are a million things that can go wrong.'

Robin McKie, Ed Vulliamy and Peter Beaumont, 2 February 2003

Helen Sharman

(b. 30 May 1963)
British astronaut

Sheffield-born Helen Sharman became the first British astronaut in 1991 after answering a radio advert simply stating: 'Astronaut wanted – no experience necessary'. The opportunity was presented as part of Britain and Russia's joint Project Juno experiment, in which, due to a total lack of government space funding, private UK companies attempted to step in to get a Briton into space. Despite some support from British Aerospace and Interflora, they failed to raise enough money, and the project was nearly cancelled – finally Mikhail Gorbachev and the Russian government made up the difference, seeing this as a good way to mend relations with Britain. Sharman was selected from more than 13,000 applicants. Successful applicants were required to have a scientific background and good linguistic ability (they would have to learn Russian), and to be in top physical and mental condition. Sharman, a chemistry graduate working as a research technologist for Mars Confectionery, made it to the final two and went to Moscow for 18 months of gruelling preparation.

> *"There is very little difference between men and women in space.*
> Helen Sharman

On 18 May 1991, Sharman was launched into space aboard the Soyuz TM-12 craft and orbited the Earth on the Mir space station for a week before returning to Earth on 26 May. Many of the ambitious microgravity experiments planned by the British organisers for the flight had to be cancelled due to budget problems and were substituted with experiments designed by British schoolchildren.

Sharman was awarded an OBE in 1992, and remains to this day the only British astronaut who hasn't had to attain US citizenship before venturing into the heavens She continues to work as a scientist, lecturing around the globe as an ambassador for British science.

So you want to be an astronaut?

As career choices go, being an astronaut takes some beating. You get the best views in the solar system and you're lauded when you get home. However, there is some competition: for the nine astronaut vacancies last advertised by ESA (European Space Agency) there were 22,000 applicants. Nasa doesn't offer much better odds – it takes on around 100 astronauts every two years, but unless you happen to be an American citizen or are prepared to become one by living over there for five years, it's not even worth thinking about.

And before you start filling out the application form, make sure you're physically fit and no taller than 6ft 2in (1.9m) – although the shorter the better, as you'll be better equipped to handle the g-forces. You must also be between 27 and 37 years old, with blood pressure no higher than 140 over 90. If you pass all these tests, you need to choose whether to become a pilot – the ones who fly the shuttles – or a mission specialist – the ones who do the experiments up there and make sure the mission goes smoothly. If all of that doesn't put you off, here's what you need to do...

1 Work outrageously hard at school

Competition is such that nothing less than straight A's will do, particularly in maths and science. Joining the Scouts isn't a bad idea either – 64% of Nasa pilots were earning their needlecraft badge at this age

2 Go to university

Get yourself a BA in engineering, science (preferably physics) or maths from a good university

3a Join the RAF

You're going to need to put in three more years of study, preferably in aeronautics or engineering, as well as notching up a few thousand hours of flight time, preferably as a test pilot

3b Get a PhD

Or at least three years of relevant professional experience. Again, make sure you're focusing on science. Many space agencies recommend that you study other languages, particularly Russian, as a cosmonaut may be your only companion for weeks on end

4 Apply, apply, apply again

The two key characteristics that pop up again and again in reference to Nasa's and ESA's ideal astronauts are determination and motivation, so never give up

Home from home

The International Space Station

If you look up at the night sky at just the right time, on the right day, you might see what looks like an incredibly bright star hurtling through space. This impressive sight is actually the International Space Station (ISS). The idea for the ISS came about when Nasa ran out of money for its planned Space Station Freedom (a name which, thankfully, was shelved as soon as nations other than the US got involved) and linked the nascent project with Russia's planned Mir 2 space station, the European Space Agency (ESA)'s Columbus station and the Japanese Experiment Module (JEM) called Kibo.

The first segment was shot into orbit in 1998 and since then more than 20 different sections have been added, with another 11 due before its final completion date in 2010, at which time the experiments can really begin. Intended as a giant laboratory, the ISS will gather information on the biology, fluid mechanics and chemistry of microgravity, and is seen, particularly by Nasa, as a major stepping stone towards manned trips to Mars.

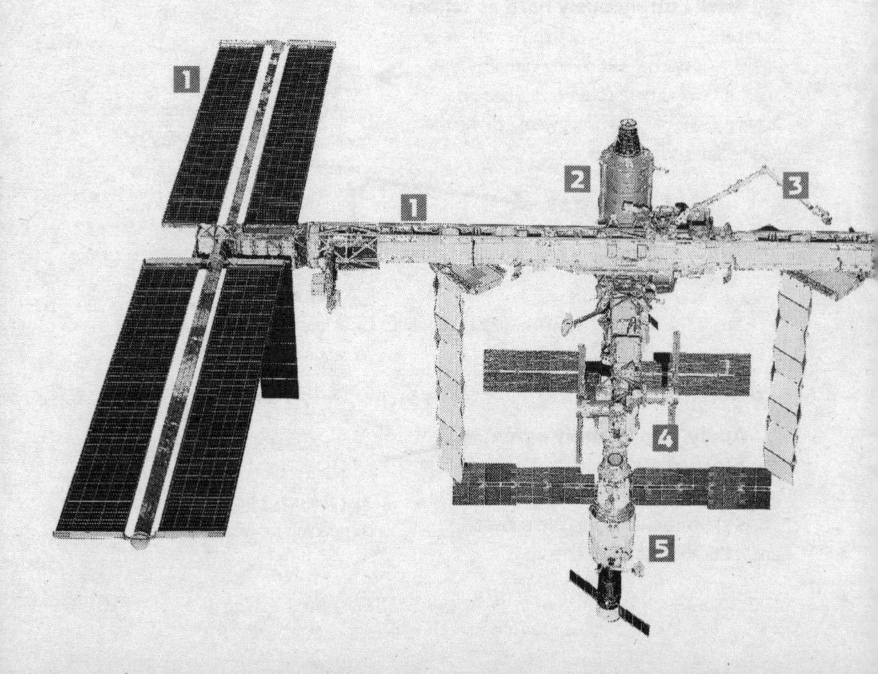

The ISS by numbers

453 tonnes Weight when completed in 2010

110m Width when completed

17,500mph Orbital speed

220 miles Altitude

2 billion km Distance travelled so far (48,000 Earth orbits)

6 months Time most astronauts spend on board

124 Number of different visitors to the ISS (including the first five space tourists)

26.2 miles Distance of the Boston Marathon, completed by astronaut Sunita Williams on a treadmill on board the ISS in March 2007. She had qualified for the race before discovering that she would be sent to the station

£63 billion Predicted cost by 2010

16 nations involved US, Russia, Canada, Japan, Brazil and 11 ESA members (Belgium, Denmark, France, Germany, Italy, Netherlands, Norway, Spain, Sweden, Switzerland and UK)

1 Integrated Truss Structure (USA, 2000-07)
Massive solar panels power the ISS while the structure holds the ISS together

2 Destiny Lab (USA, 2001)
Primary research lab for the US

3 Canadarm (Canada, 2001)
The station's robotic arm

4 Zarya Control Module (Russia and USA, 1998)
Provides battery power, fuel storage and docking capability. It was the first piece of the ISS in space

5 Zvezda Service Module (Russia, 2000)
Provides living quarters and life-support systems

The insider: astrophysicist

Ofer Lahav

I suppose the first things that got me interested in the science of space were the Apollo missions. When man landed on the Moon in 1969 I was 10 years old, and I got very excited about the possibilities of exploring space and understanding where we are in the cosmos (not that I wanted to go up there – I was always more interested in exploring it from our little planet).

I still feel that sense of excitement just looking at the sky, especially when I go away from the city lights to a dark site in the desert or when we go to one of the observatories in Chile or Australia. Whether one is a child or an adult, an amateur astronomer or a professional, there is a joy in just seeing it. As an astronomer, I put it in a wider context, so instead of just a dot in the sky I see a whole nebula or galaxy. So the sense of wonder is even greater.

> *“I'm astounded by people who want to know the universe when it's hard enough to find your way around Chinatown.*
> Woody Allen

In terms of scientific progress, the past 100 years were absolutely remarkable. To put it in perspective, 100 years ago people still thought that the whole universe was just our Milky Way, and now we know that there are billions of galaxies out there and we are just one of them. I think what happened was the sudden progress of technology – we could use bigger and better telescopes. In the Twenties, Edwin Hubble and his associates used these telescopes to discover that what were then known as merely nebulae were so far away that they had to be separate galaxies.

However, to say it was just technology is misleading. Just a few years before Hubble, Einstein formulated his theory of relativity, in which he figured out that the universe could be contracting, expanding or static – it's remarkable that someone can sit with nothing but a pencil and paper and understand how the universe works. So I think it's a combination of technology and the power of the human brain; I think the miracle of the last 100 years was that these two things came together – Hubble's measurements proved that the universe was expanding.

My own area of research is based around the cosmological constant and dark energy, undoubtedly one of the biggest questions – not only in astronomy, but also in the history of physics. Present measurements show that the stuff we're made of, atoms, accounts for only 4% of the universe. There is another 21% or so of dark matter, while the other 75% is dark energy. It's still a mystery to us – we don't quite know what it is – but it's all very exciting. Here at University College London we're involved in a number of international projects to address that very problem: for example, we're part of the Dark Energy Survey, which will map 300 million galaxies in an attempt to heighten our knowledge of dark energy.

Astrophysics requires plenty of imagination, but also new data is always coming in. If you came up with a crazy idea, we'd say: 'OK, let's compare it with the measurements...' In this way many ideas are rejected, but the observations could also be wrong. So it's a detective story, a Sherlock Holmes story. **OFER LAHAV**

Professor Ofer Lahav is head of Astrophysics and Perren Chair of Astronomy at University College London. He was recently part of an international effort to construct a 3D map of more than a million galaxies, and is at the forefront of research into dark matter

Five big questions in astrophysics

1 What is dark matter? We know it's out there, and the effect it may be having on the universe; we just don't know what it is.

2 Can we tame a nuclear-fusion reaction? Nuclear fusion, the process that fuels the Sun, is more efficient than nuclear fission. Figuring out how to harness it could solve our power problems.

3 What was there before the Big Bang? The biggest question of all.

4 What happens at the edge of a black hole? Understanding what goes on at its mysterious core and surrounding environs provides a rather tricky problem.

5 What are the preconditions for life to emerge? Finding out what life needs to evolve from simple matter into organisms could also tell us whether there might be life elsewhere.

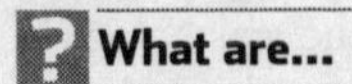

Black holes

Black holes are not really holes but the leftover remnants of massive, burnt-out stars that are packed with particularly dense matter that creates such an exceptionally strong gravitational force that nothing can escape its surface – not even light (hence black hole). These phenomena occur at the centre of large galaxies or when a giant star collapses and shrinks during the final phases of its life.

> *God not only plays dice, He also sometimes throws the dice where they cannot be seen.*
> Stephen Hawking

Anything that approaches a black hole is first torn apart by its immense gravitational force, then squashed into a flat rotating disc that spirals into the hole. The friction caused as it spins burns up the material, and it smashes into pieces as it enters the core of the hole. Einstein's theory of general relativity offers an explanation for the presence of black holes. The theory predicts that when a large enough amount of mass is present within a sufficiently small region of space, all paths through space are warped, forcing all matter and radiation to fall inwards.

Black holes are thought to be transient entities, not the fixed abysses marked on galaxy maps in sci-fi movies. Professor Stephen Hawking's theory – Hawking radiation – is that because of quantum mechanical effects, black holes emit thermal radiation and that the energy which produces the radiation comes from its mass. Consequently the black hole gradually shrinks, burning off its mass until it vanishes entirely. The centre of a black hole is known as a singularity, similar to the one that existed before the Big Bang, and is infinitely dense and incomprehensibly tiny.

The event horizon is the limit beyond which not even light can escape. Therefore if two astronauts stood in front of it, the one who walked over the line would immediately become invisible to the other. After reaching this point, it would be impossible for any known particle to escape, and it would take just a few seconds for the astronaut to be pulled into the oblivion at the core. **Robin McKie**

Ten space records

Longest single spaceflight Valeriy Polyakov spent 437 days, 17 hours and 58 minutes aboard the Mir space station in 1994, travelling 300,765,000km in total.

Most time in space overall Sergei Krikalev has spent a total of 803 days, nine hours and 39 minutes in space. His first mission was to the Mir space station in 1988 and he is expected to become the first person to have stayed aboard the International Space Station three times.

Most time in space overall (by country) Russia's citizens have spent a total of 17,421.32 days in space. The USA is lagging behind with just over 10,000 days.

Longest time in space for an animal The unnamed tortoises of the USSR's 1975 mission spent 90.5 days floating around in space.

Longest time spent on the Moon Gene Cernan and Harrison Schmitt spent 74 hours, 59 minutes and 40 seconds on the surface during the Apollo 17 mission in 1972.

Fastest men alive The crew of Apollo 10 (Thomas Stafford, John Young and Gene Cernan) reached a speed of 39,897km/h in May 1969, the fastest ever attained by humans.

Furthest humans from Earth The crew of Apollo 13 (James Lovell, Fred Haise and John Swigert) were 400,171km from Earth while passing over the far side of the Moon in April 1970.

Oldest person in space John Glenn was 77 years old when he flew on the space shuttle Discovery in October 1998.

Youngest person in space Gherman Titov was 25 years old when he orbited the Earth around 20 times aboard Vostok 2 in August 1961.

Most spacewalks Anatoly Solovyev made 16 spacewalks, totalling 77 hours and 41 minutes, the longest time that anyone has spent on spacewalks.

Myths of our solar system

The cosmos we now confront is awesome, but one with little place for humanity's story. The stars that inspired myth-makers and poets turn out to be balls of gas burning through nuclear-fusion reactions. In the words of astronomer Richard Grossinger: 'The beauty of space is overshadowed by the sense that it is nothing but a noisy brute.'

Yet stars and planets, even newly discovered, still carry classical mythology, which Jungian psychology has rediscovered as 'archetypes' of the human psyche, and which astrologers obstinately continue to interpret. The cosmologies of other cultures – Chinese, Mayan, Aborigine – and of science fiction have added layers of meaning to classical and mediaeval views of the spiritual heavens.

The Sun Usually imagined as a life-giving god – Ra (Egypt), Helios (Greece) – the Sun is female in Celtic and Norse myth. Early Christianity linked the Sun to Christ, who took over solar festivals like the Winter solstice. Heroic light-bringers – take a bow, Luke Skywalker – are also linked to solar mythology.

The Moon Greece and Rome made the Moon powerfully female – Artemis Selena, Hecate, Diana – but for Babylon and Egypt, the Moon was a male god. More myths and folklore cling to our nearest neighbour than to any other celestial body, thanks to its connection to the tides, the menstrual cycle and agriculture. And everyone has heard a werewolf's call at full Moon, if only in the cinema.

Mercury The quicksilver planet is invariably a messenger, scribe, wisdom-bringer and shape-shifter: Nabu (Babylon), Thoth (Egypt), Hermes (Greece) and Odin (Norse). These days Mercury is the speedy courier service or fast outboard motor.

Venus For science Venus is 'Earth's evil twin', a toxic stew of sulphuric acid, but by tradition her green glow makes her a goddess: Ishtar (Babylon), Aphrodite (Greece), Venus (Rome). Even early 20th-century astronomy imagined a planet of dinosaurs and primal swamps. Oops.

Mars For the ancient world, Mars was a warrior who loved conflict for its own sake, a dangerous energy that threatened peace. Mars has menaced the modern age in HG Wells' *War of the Worlds* and the film *Mars Attacks*. That there is 'Life on Mars' remains an obsession of science and fiction.

Jupiter The various sky gods linked to the giant planet – Zeus, Thor, Jupiter – were mostly beneficent law bringers. What mediaeval cosmologers deemed 'the greater benefic' remains today's booming financial fund, and the destination in the cryptic *2001: A Space Odyssey*. Jupiter's moons (at least 16) are popular sci-fi playgrounds.

Saturn As the slowest-moving planet (until Uranus' discovery), Saturn (the Greek Cronos) was the solar system's timekeeper. As Old Father Time, Saturn is both builder and destroyer, while his myth – a despot who consumes his children – is the archetype of the bad father. In ancient cosmology, Saturn was feared as a bringer of pestilence.

Uranus Originally named 'Georgium' after King George III. Ouranos was Saturn's despotic father, his myth wildly at odds with astrology's interpretation of Uranus as the planet of revolution. Unlike his consort, the earth goddess Gaia, Uranus has not caught on with the public, his name a hostage to fortune. Not to be confused with Urania, muse of astronomy and astrology.

Neptune The Roman ruler of the oceans (Poseidon to Greece) remains an earthly rather than a cosmic deity, commonly frolicking with mermaids. As a planet it has yet to capture public imagination, though several sci-fi novels, like Jeff Carver's *Neptune Crossing*, focus on its largest moon, Triton.

Sedna Named for the Inuit goddess of the deep (because it's in deep space, naturally), Sedna is the first planet to break the Greco-Roman name barrier. Her myth variously portrays her as insatiable monster and protector of marine life.

Eris For two years planet 2003UB313 was the first to be named after a TV deity – Xena, the warrior princess – until she was renamed as the Greek goddess of strife on account of the trouble her discovery caused at the International Astronomical Union. **Neil Spencer**

The Observer archive: historic moments in space exploration

Searching for life on Mars

(25 January 2004)

Scientists believe that they may soon discover lakes beneath the arid surface of Mars. Some of these subterranean pools could provide homes for primitive life forms.

Researchers' hopes of finding liquid water on Mars have been raised by the dramatic discovery that Europe's Mars Express has discovered evidence of ice on the planet's surface only a week after turning on its instruments. The discovery has sent European space scientists into raptures after having had their spirits dashed by the failure of Mars Express's lander, Beagle 2, to communicate with Earth after its scheduled landing on Christmas Day.

> *"Life, for ever dying to be born afresh, for ever young and eager, will presently stand upon this Earth as upon a footstool, and stretch out its realm amidst the stars.*
>
> HG Wells

'Finding anything that has to do with water on Mars is a sort of holy grail,' said David Southwood, science director of the European Space Agency. 'This is better than anything we've had so far.'

Ice was detected by two separate instruments on board the orbiting probe: Omega, which maps chemicals on the surface, and an instrument called a PFS, which studies the spectrum of molecules. Both began operating on 18 January. However, the Mars Express instrument likely to provide the most exciting data has yet to be switched on. The Marsis radar altimeter, which is not scheduled for activation until April, will map the structure of Mars to a depth of several miles. Ancient caverns filled with water, which could provide homes for living beings, could be pinpointed this way.

'We know that microbes can survive in Antarctic ice at -40C,' said Mars Express researcher Martin Siegert of Bristol University. 'Even at that temperature, water rich in chemicals forms at the boundaries between ice crystals, and we have found bacteria there. However,

the best prospects for life on Mars probably lie underground, where geothermal energy could keep water nice and warm.'

At the same time, scientists working on Mars Express's high-resolution stereo camera will work on creating a 3-D map of the entire planet by the year 2007. Using that, they will then be able to pinpoint the most promising surface sites to find water. 'Until now, we have only had flat, two-dimensional images of Mars,' said Professor Jan-Peter Muller of University College, London. 'Now we have pictures from which we can make positive geological predictions. This is going to change our understanding of the surface of the planet.'

The good fortune of Europe's scientists contrasts with the sudden gloom that has enveloped Nasa engineers, who were last night struggling to revive their ailing Mars rover, Spirit, and preparing for the landing of its twin, Opportunity, which was scheduled to touch down this morning. Spirit, which together with Opportunity cost £500 million, began to malfunction on Wednesday, nearly three weeks after landing on Mars's Gusev Crater and after sending back streams of data and pictures. For the following two days, it transmitted only sporadic beeps but began to transmit more coherent signals on Friday, though its prognosis remains uncertain. 'The chances that it will be perfect again are not good,' said project manager Pete Theisinger at Nasa's Jet Propulsion Laboratory. Even under the best of circumstances, the rover will not be back to normal for weeks, he added. ...

Engineers believe hardware damage has wreaked havoc with Spirit's software, forcing it to reboot its computer 60 times. But Theisinger urged his team not to dwell on Spirit's problems and to stay focused on Opportunity.

Its target is the Meridiani Planum, a dark grey region which is believed to be rich in the mineral grey haematite which typically forms in water-rich environments. However, Opportunity is unlikely to start investigating for a while. Spirit took two weeks to roll on to the Martian soil. Opportunity may take much longer as scientists react with heightened caution following their first rover's breakdown, a delay that will reduce the three-month mission's scientific returns.

Robin McKie, 25 January 2004

Now Mars probe hunts for oceans

...opean scientists in raptures at prospect of primitive life

Call to sc...

asylum a...

Burt Rutan

(b. 17 June 1943)

Engineer, inventor and space tourism pioneer

Elbert 'Burt' Rutan is the chief designer and CEO of Scaled Composites, the aerospace company which in 2004 won the inaugural $10 million (£5m) X Prize with its SpaceShipOne spacecraft – the first privately built, flown and funded craft to reach space. This momentous achievement turned affordable space tourism from a dream into a reality.

The Oregon-born aviation obsessive found his first major success with the Voyager aircraft, which in 1986 successfully achieved the first-ever nonstop flight around the world. It now hangs in the Smithsonian National Air and Space Museum alongside the Wright Flyer (the first powered aircraft) and the Spirit of St Louis (the first aircraft to fly across the Atlantic). Rutan has since smashed Voyager's record (nine days, three minutes, 44 seconds) with the GlobalFlyer, which made the trip in less than four days as well as setting the record for the longest flight in history by an aircraft (26,389 miles).

> *"At first, it will be real rich people, hundreds of them, flying into suborbital space. But what will happen is you'll run out of real rich people real quickly.*
>
> Burt Rutan

Rutan specialises in dealing with incredibly lightweight materials – he likes to tell his designers that, on finishing a part, they should throw it up in the air and 'if it comes down, it's too heavy'. This ethos has led him to build the environmentally friendly 100mpg Ultralite car for General Motors, and he is now working with Virgin Galactic on their SpaceShipTwo passenger spacecraft as well as with the Transformational Space Corporation on a 'space taxi' to the International Space Station. His importance to aviation and the future of spaceflight led *Time* magazine to include him in their list of the 100 Most Influential People in 2005.

They came from outer space

What the 12 moonwalkers did next

1 Neil Armstrong (pictured right) Apollo 11 (Set foot on the Moon 21 July 1969)
Armstrong, possibly the most remote and enigmatic of all the astronauts to reach the Moon, was never comfortable with the hero status afforded to him by the media and the world at large. He shunned public appearances, interviews and lucrative commercial endorsements to focus instead on teaching and his continued work with Nasa. He retired from Nasa in 1971 and now lives quietly with his wife in Ohio – and still refuses to sign autographs.

2 Buzz Aldrin Apollo 11 (21 July 1969)
Returning to terrestrial life proved challenging, and Mike Collins (the third member of the Apollo 11 mission) said of Aldrin in 1972: 'Fame has not worn well on Buzz. I think he resents not being the first man on the Moon more than he appreciates being the second.' He soon fell into a cycle of alcoholism and depression, leaving his job with the military and going through two bitter divorces, only beginning his recovery with his third wife Lois Driggs in 1988. Now a novelist and long-term advocate of privatised space tourism, Aldrin has satisfied his lust for adventure by joining the expedition to explore the Titanic and by going to the North Pole.

3 Charles 'Pete' Conrad Apollo 12 (19 November 1969)
One of the more charismatic of all the lunar visitors, Conrad – whose first word on the Moon was 'Whoopee!' – left Nasa in 1974 to move into the private sector, working towards the development of commercial space travel with aviation giant McDonnell-Douglas. He died in a motorcycle accident in 1999, 30 years after commanding Apollo 12.

4 Alan Bean Apollo 12 (19 November 1969)
Bean remained at Nasa for 12 years after Apollo 12, retiring in 1981 to devote himself full time to painting. Now he paints breathtaking lunar scenes over and over again. With one painting that shows him standing triumphant on a lunar surface coloured with a euphoric

haze of greens, violets and golds, Bean answered journalists' most frequently asked question: he named the self-portrait 'That's How It Felt to Walk on the Moon'.

5 Alan Shepard Apollo 14 (5 February 1971)
The first American in space in May 1961 and the fifth on the moon 10 years later, Shepard was nicknamed 'the icy commander' – he was a fearsome figure with a strong military background. Walking on the Moon's surface, however, made him do something nobody expected: he cried. He returned to Earth a calmer man and retired from Nasa in 1974 to enter the private sector. He died of leukaemia in 1998.

6 Edgar Mitchell Apollo 14 (5 February 1971)
He claimed that seeing the Earth from the Moon gave him a sense of 'universal connectedness'. He left Nasa soon after his return and in 1973 formed the Institute of Noetic Sciences, which was devoted to the research of spiritual energy, alternative healing and psychic abilities. He claimed in 2004 that a teenage 'healer' in Vancouver cured his cancer from thousands of miles away, and has pleaded with Washington for years to tell the truth about aliens, which he believes have been visiting Earth for decades.

7 David Scott Apollo 15 (30 July 1971)
Embroiled in the postage-stamp scandal – in which the crew of Apollo 15 carried 398 commemorative stamp covers to the Moon with the understanding that a German dealer would buy 100 of them for an exorbitant price – Scott became Congress' sacrificial lamb and was banned from ever revisiting space. He retired from Nasa in 1975 and all but disappeared, only emerging when newsreader Anna Ford announced her engagement to him in 2003. It didn't last, and Scott – still haunted by the scandal – now lives in London and works as a motivational speaker.

8 James Irwin Apollo 15 (30 July 1971)
While Conrad whooped in pure ecstasy and Bean saw the lunar surface erupt into colourful life, Irwin, while bouncing at the feet of the Moon's Apennine Mountains, heard God whispering to him. It changed him forever. On returning to Earth, he left Nasa – avoiding the postage-stamp scandal – for the church,

founding the High Flight evangelical ministry, with which he led several unsuccessful missions to Turkey in search of Noah's Ark. Irwin died in 1991.

9 John W Young Apollo 16 (21 April 1972)
The first person to make six space flights – still a record – Young spent the next 32 years at Nasa before retiring in 2004 at the age of 74. Playing a part in almost every major Nasa development and launch in its 50-year history, from Gemini to the Space Shuttle, he was once described by a fellow astronaut as 'truly a fascinating man, whose modesty is matched only by the scale of his own achievements'.

10 Charles Duke Apollo 16 (21 April 1972)
Duke, who had felt so at home on the Moon he reportedly had to resist the urge to take his helmet off, became one of the biggest victims of the moonwalkers' curse: boredom. He left Nasa and decided to make a lot of money. He did it by selling beer, then grew bored and started drinking beer. It was his wife Dotty who felt the brunt of the Moon's malign influence: her husband had a fiery temper and became distant and engulfed in his work. She turned to drink and drugs, and then to God. Duke followed her into religion, giving up his beer-distribution business. They remain a devout couple.

11 Eugene Cernan Apollo 17 (11 December 1972)
Cernan, the born astronaut and last man on the Moon, moved into the private sector in 1975. He still works with Nasa, helping to design and build new projects. Now one of the most vocal of all Apollo astronauts, he maintains his passion for manned spaceflight and makes regular public appearances, urging a mission back to the Moon and even to Mars.

12 Harrison 'Jack' Schmitt Apollo 17 (11 December 1972)
A scientist with a fearsome intellect, Schmitt left Nasa in 1975 to enter the world of politics. He was elected as a Republican senator for New Mexico in 1977 and served one term before he was defeated in 1982. He quit politics and now devotes most of his time to working towards a better understanding of helium-3, a potential source of clean energy which is found in abundance on the Moon.

Ongoing missions

What's currently in space

Pioneer 10 (launched in 1972) Designed to study Jupiter and its moons. We lost radio contact in 2003, but it is now on its way to the star Aldebaran, which it should reach in 2 million years.

Voyager 1 (1977) The most distant man-made object from Earth, hurtling out of our solar system at 500m km/year, Voyager 1 is now at the edge of the heliosphere, more than 13 billion km away. With its sister probe Voyager 2 (also launched in 1977), the probe has returned more new knowledge about the outer planets than had existed in all of the preceding history of astronomy. It will reach Alpha Centauri in 40,000 years, carrying gold records – designed by Carl Sagan – holding some of the great musical and artistic achievements of humanity, as well as voices in hundreds of languages saying hello.

Hubble Space Telescope (1990) Fixed in 1993 after bad quality control during its manufacture gave it about the same resolution as that of a blurry garden telescope, Hubble has since sent back some of the most beautiful pictures of the universe yet seen.

SOHO (Solar and Heliospheric Observatory) (1995) This joint ESA/Nasa project studies space weather from Earth's orbit.

Cassini-Huygens mission (1997) Studying Saturn and its moons – it flew past Titan in October 2007.

International Space Station (2000) To be completed in 2010.

WMAP (Wilkinson Microwave Anisotropy Probe) (2001) A probe that has discovered the accurate age of the universe (to the nearest 0.2 billion years), what the universe is composed of and how fast it is expanding (the Hubble constant).

Mars Exploration Rovers (2003) Spirit and Opportunity have been driving around the planet's surface for four years, providing us with massive amounts of new information about the red planet.

Messenger (2004) Due to become the first probe to orbit Mercury in 2011, it will test theories that the planet may be shrinking.

Mars Reconnaissance Orbiter (2005) Currently orbiting Mars,

analysing its surface, it found evidence in early 2007 that water or liquid carbon dioxide did at some stage exist on Mars.

Deep Impact (2005) The first to land on a comet to study its properties in more depth. It's going to fly back past Earth in December 2007 on its way to study planets outside our solar system and other comets.

New Horizons (2006) Nasa probe designed to fly by and study Pluto and its moons. It is expected to reach Pluto in 2015.

Dawn (2007) Launched in September 2007, Dawn will be the first spacecraft to orbit two different bodies when it visits Vesta and Ceres, two of the largest asteroids in the solar system, in 2015.

Kaguya (2007) The Japanese probe entered lunar orbit in early October 2007 to discover the origins and evolution of the Moon. It also took the first-ever high-definition picture of Earth from outer space.

And plans for the future...

Chandrayaan 1 An unmanned lunar orbital probe that will be India's first trip to the Moon, expected to launch in spring 2008.

Mars Science Laboratory The most advanced Mars rover ever launched, by 2010 this robot will discover whether Mars can support life.

Orion Set to take over the duties of the Space Shuttle – due to be phased out by 2010 – Orion will at first take Nasa astronauts to the International Space Station. However, by 2020 it's hoped it will be a key, reusable component in a manned mission to the Moon and Mars.

James Webb Space Telescope Designed in collaboration between Nasa, ESA and the Canadian Space Agency, this telescope will replace the ageing Hubble in 2013, searching for light from the first stars and galaxies to have formed after the Big Bang.

Shenzhou There have already been six Shenzhou missions launched by the Chinese, with at least four more planned for the next two years with the hope of reaching the Moon's orbit by 2015 – and after that a manned mission is probably not far behind.

Darwin An ESA telescopic craft designed to hunt for Earth-like planets orbiting nearby stars. It will be heading spaceward by 2015.

A bang or a whimper

How the universe will end

Scientists are now largely in agreement about how the universe began (though the Big Bang is by no means the only theory we have), but ask a group of boffins how the universe will end and be prepared for an apocalyptic argument. There are three main theories...

1 Equilibrium

The universe will expand merrily until it finally halts at a point infinitely far into the future. In other words, it'll all be fine. This theory commands possibly the most broad scientific support.

2 The Big Crunch

If there is too much matter in the universe, its expansion will slow and finally stop due to the massive gravitational pull of all this mass. The universe will not just stop there, though, but quickly reverse, pulling all matter back into the infinitely hot, infinitely dense singularity that existed before the Big Bang. Some think there would then be another Big Bang, giving the impression that the universe constantly expands, contracts then bounces out again in a cyclical fashion. One leading physicist claims we've only got 10 to 20 billion years before this happens, meaning our universe has just reached its calm middle age, with the rapidly expanding waistline to go with it.

3 The Big Chill

If there isn't enough matter in the universe to halt its accelerating expansion and either stall it in a happy equilibrium or pull it all back together, everything will continue to expand forever. Matter will be spread incredibly thinly over vast distances and stars will burn out while galaxies lose their ability to form new ones and the universe will reach temperatures approaching absolute zero. Although it will never quite end, the universe will become a wasteland of dust and dead stars. Probably the most depressing of all apocalypse scenarios, it means the universe will go out with a cold whimper, stretching into eternity.